The
Mensa
Puzzle
Book

THIS IS A CARLTON BOOK

This edition published in 2018 by
Carlton Books Ltd
20 Mortimer Street
London W1T 3JW

ISBN: 978-1-78739-185-7

10 9 8 7 6 5 4 3 2 1

Printed in Denmark

The Mensa Puzzle Book

The World's Toughest Puzzles from
the World's Smartest Organisation

CARLTON
BOOKS

Contents

Introduction to Mensa

The first and biggest organisation for people with a high IQ, Mensa has been bringing intelligent people together from all over the world for decades. Our mission is three-fold:

- to identify and to foster human intelligence for the benefit of humanity;
- to encourage research into the nature, characteristics, and uses of intelligence; and
- to provide a stimulating intellectual and social environment for our members.

The only requirement for membership that Mensa has ever had is to score at or above 98% in an approved standardised IQ test. Even our name was chosen to highlight our egalitarian spirit – the Latin word mensa means "table", and represents the theoretical round table at which we all sit as equals, regardless of age, gender, race, or status. We are non-political, nonreligious, and non-discriminatory in every sense – except for IQ, of course!

There are now well over 130,000 Mensans in countries around the globe. More than 50 nations have their own national Mensa organisations, and for the rest, Mensa International serves as an umbrella covering the entire planet. Antarctica is the only continent without any members, but then so far, the continent has no permanent residents. The youngest person to join British Mensa was the UK's Elise Tan-Roberts, who became a Mensan at the age of just two years and four months, while our oldest member to date was 103, and didn't join until she was in her 90s.

Similarly, our membership ranges from people who didn't achieve highly at school to professors with multiple doctorates, and includes programmers, truck drivers, artists, farmers, soldiers, musicians, fire fighters, models, scientists, builders, writers, fishermen, accountants, boxers, and police officers. Some are world-famous names, whilst others are totally outside the public's awareness. It doesn't matter in Mensa – all are equal.

As a high IQ society, Mensa has a core interest in intelligence – what it is, how to nurture it, and how to make the most of it. We are a strictly non-profit organisation, and are involved with numerous programs for gifted children, improving literacy, and making education accessible. The Mensa Foundation regularly publishes a scientific journal of research into relevant scientific areas. But we are also a social group, and bringing intelligent people together is very important to us.

Mensa holds a lot of events for its members at all levels from the local to the international. There are regular local and regional gatherings in towns and cities all over the world, ranging from semi-formal meet-ups to lectures, tour groups, dinner and lunch sessions, and nights of cinema, theatre, or gaming. In some larger cities, there are events available most days. Lots of national Mensa organisations also arrange frequent countrywide meetings, including spectacular annual gatherings with workshops, speakers, dance evenings, games, children's events, and much more. They also issue national membership magazines, such as British Mensa's Mensa Magazine, and American Mensa's Mensa Bulletin, both monthly.

But members also come together frequently to share common ground. These special interest groups (SIGs) cover all manner of subject that you can imagine, from the everyday to the extremely obscure. SIGs issue regular bulletins and zines, and many also organise meet-ups, provide email discussion lists, and more. If you can't find a particular interest group that you're looking for, starting one yourself is extremely simple.

Simply put, Mensa can be as large or small a part of your life as you like. For some members, the organisation is a family, full of friends; Mensa marriages have taken place. For others, it is a casual interest, a little something to help get the grey matter ticking over. Wherever you might fall on that spectrum, it's fine. We're all equal, remember.

We do encourage all our members to use their brains, of course. Mental exercise is not just a lot of fun, it can definitely be of help in keeping the mind fit and healthy. Research over the last decade has clearly demonstrated that regular puzzle solving and social interaction can help to actively stave off Alzheimer's disease. The brain remains responsive to the ways we use it all through our lives – a principle called neuroplasticity – so the more we challenge it, the stronger our abilities to meet those challenges will become.

Besides, solving puzzles and answering tricky questions are amongst the most basic of human behaviours. You find recreational puzzles, games and riddles in every culture around the world, and in every time period we have half-decent archaeological remains from. It's a core need, and something we work hard to encourage.

At the end of the day though, Mensa is about you – take what you want from us, and ignore the rest. We're here for you, not the other way around.

Introduction to The Mensa Puzzle Book

Puzzles have been part of human culture for thousands of years and they are ubiquitous; there is no culture, current or historic, of whom we have a large amount of knowledge that has not included puzzles in some form or another. Even the very earliest writings include clear evidence of them.

There are good reasons for this. The first, and most obvious, is that puzzles are enjoyable. Our brains are hard-wired to enjoy being challenged, and the pleasurable mental exercise puzzles produce is the reason why you will see so many people fervently attempting to finish a Sudoku before the end of their morning commute.

Secondly, and perhaps most importantly, numerous studies have shown that regularly participating in some form of mental exercise – puzzles, for example – helps not just to improve cognitive abilities but, crucially, to stave off mental decline as you age. In a world in which humans are living longer and longer lives, the key to enjoying the fruits of your retirement lie in keeping your mental edge. So no matter what your intellectual goals are, mental stimulation from well-designed puzzles can be immensely useful.

The Mensa Puzzle Book itself contains around 400 puzzles divided into nine different chapters. Five of these include black and white puzzles and four contain colour puzzles, to add an extra dimension into the mix. You will find that each chapter has a wide variety of puzzles, and this is for good reason. Different puzzles test different areas of your mental faculties including logical reasoning, deductive inference, spatial awareness, mathematic abilities, word patterns and many more. The puzzles in *The Mensa Puzzle Book* have been chosen to give your brain an all-around workout. Furthermore, the puzzles increase in difficulty as the book progresses. The intention is that as you work through, chapter by chapter, your abilities should increase accordingly until you feel comfortable taking on the challenge of the final puzzle mix.

Ultimately, the purpose of this book is not just to provide a stern test, but also a great deal of enjoyment in the process of solving the challenges within.

Mensa is the international society for people with a high IQ. We have more than 100,000 members in over 40 countries worldwide.

The society's aims are:
to identify and foster human intelligence for the benefit of humanity to encourage research in the nature, characteristics, and uses of intelligence to provide a stimulating intellectual and social environment for its members.

Anyone with an IQ score in the top two per cent of population is eligible to become a member of Mensa – are you the 'one in 50' we've been looking for?

Mensa membership offers an excellent range of benefits:
Networking and social activities nationally and around the world Special Interest Groups – hundreds of chances to pursue your hobbies and interests – from art to zoology!
Monthly members' magazine and regional newsletters Local meetings – from games challenges to food and drink National and international weekend gatherings and conferences Intellectually stimulating lectures and seminars Access to the worldwide SIGHT network for travellers and hosts

For more information about Mensa: www.mensa.org, or

British Mensa Ltd.,
St John's House,
St John's Square,
Wolverhampton
WV2 4AH
Telephone: +44 (0) 1902 772771
E-mail: enquiries@mensa.org.uk
www.mensa.org.uk

Puzzle Mix 1

Puzzle 1 – Sudoku

	7	6				9	8	
5	8	9				6	2	1
1		2				7		5
	5			6			9	
			5	8	2			
2			7		8			9
3		8		5		1		7
	9						3	

Puzzle 2

Move from square to touching square, including diagonals, to discover the longest possible country name from these letters.

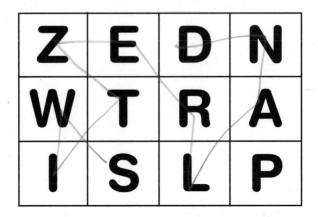

Answers see page 300

Puzzle 3

Divide the diamond into four identical shapes, each containing one of each of the following five symbols:

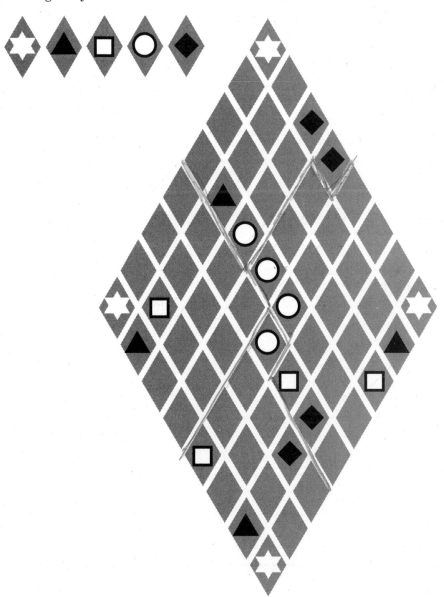

Answer see page 300

Puzzle 4

Arrange the tiles in this diagram so that they form a square. When this is done correctly four words can be read down and across. What are the words?

Puzzle 5

Insert the correct mathematical signs between each number in order to resolve the equation. What are the signs?

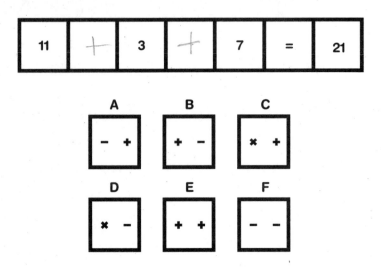

Answers see page 300-1

Puzzle 6

Draw three straight lines that will give you six sections with one clock, two hares and three lightning bolts in each section.

Answer see page 301

Puzzle 7

Can you find the 20 creatures in the word search below?

Ape	Dog	Hen	Moose
Badger	Fish	Lion	Pig
Bear	Gnu	Llama	Rat
Boa	Goat	Mink	Tiger
Deer	Hamster	Mole	Yak

A	B	K	A	Y	N	E	H
R	E	G	I	T	T	P	A
L	A	K	N	B	O	A	M
I	R	A	T	U	O	M	S
O	H	E	K	I	T	O	T
N	S	N	G	A	G	L	E
P	I	G	O	D	E	E	R
M	F	G	A	M	A	L	L
E	S	O	O	M	V	B	E

Answer see page 301

Puzzle 8 – Sudoku

3			2			7		
	4				9	2		
	7		4					6
8	3						9	
				5				
	5						2	3
7					4		6	
		4	1				5	
		8			7			1

Puzzle 9

I live at the beginning of eternity;

At the end of time and space;

I am the beginning of every end,

And the end of every place.

Who am I ?

Answers see page 301-2

Puzzle 10

Insert the missing numbers. In each pattern the missing number has something to do with the surrounding numbers in some combination.

A

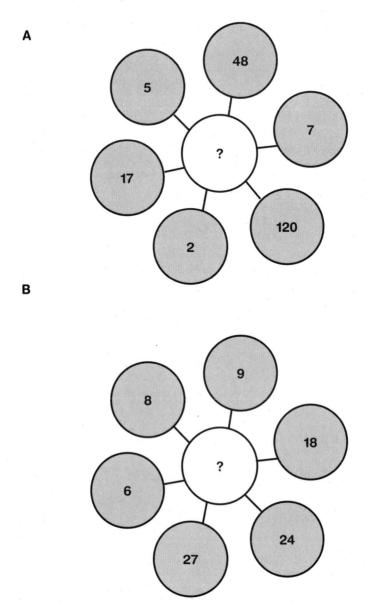

B

Answers see page 302

Puzzle 11

Six of the words in the diagram are associated for some reason. Find the words and then work out whether SHELL belongs to the group.

BEAST
DECOR
HERON
BATON
HUMAN

ADDER
PILAF
PYGMY
TAXIS
ROUND

Puzzle 12

Find the starting point and move from square to adjoining square, horizontally or vertically, but not diagonally, to spell a 12-letter word, using each letter once only. What are the missing letters?

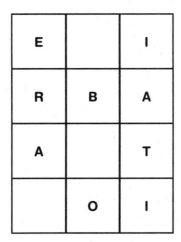

E		I
R	B	A
A		T
	O	I

Answers see page 302

Puzzle 13

Here's a trick one.

How many months have 30 days?

Puzzle 14 – Sudoku

2								
	6		1	3	7		9	
			2	8			3	
6	2		3			4		7
		8		2		6		
9		7			8		2	1
	8			7	1			
	3		5	9	2		4	
								5

Answers see page 303

Puzzle 15

How many bricks are missing from this wall?

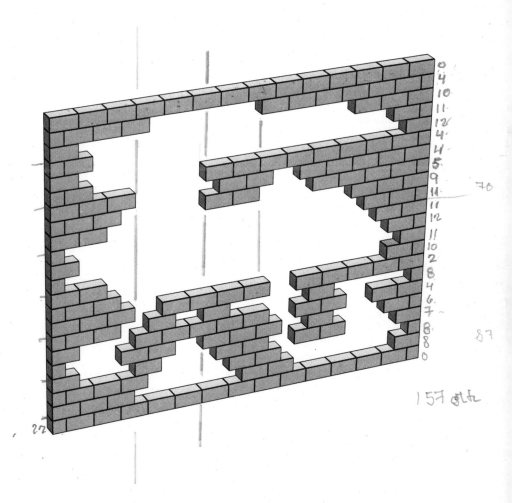

Answer see page 303

Puzzle 16

Make a circle out of these shapes. When the correct circle has been found an English word can be read clockwise. What is the word?

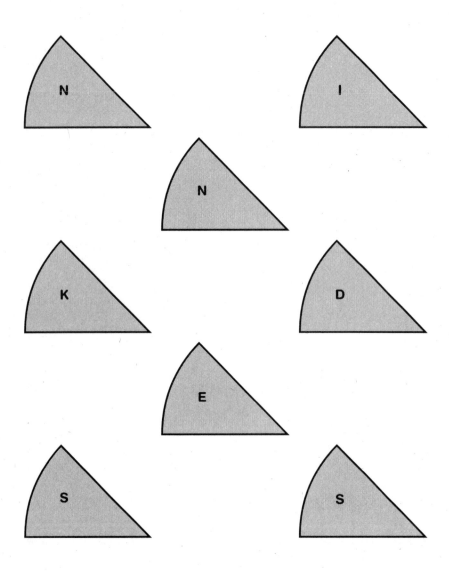

Answer see page 303

Puzzle 17

Here is an unusual safe. Each of the buttons must be pressed only once in the correct order to open it. The last button is marked F. The number of moves and the direction is marked on each button. Thus 1U would mean one move up, while 1L would mean one move to the left. Using the grid reference, which button is the first you must press?

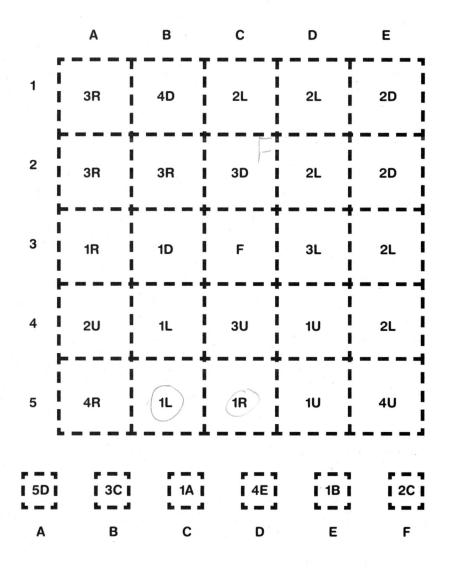

Answer see page 304

Puzzle 18

Look at the three shapes. Does option A, B, C, D or E continue the sequence?

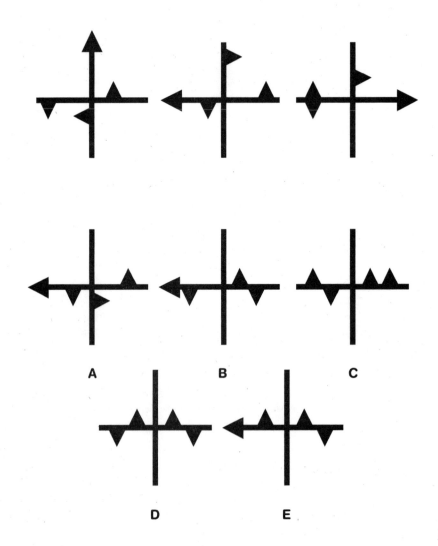

A   **B**   **C**

D   **E**

Answer see page 304

Puzzle 19

The black dots represent hinge points. If points A and B are moved together, will points C and D move together or apart?

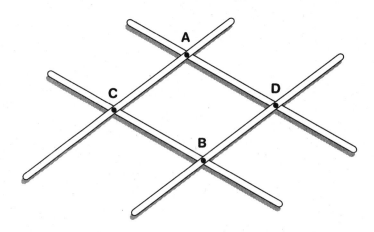

Puzzle 20 – Sudoku

8						2		1
	3		1					
6				2		5		
					6	8		9
			3	4	8			
					5	3		2
2				7		6		
	9		8					
1						4		3

Answers see page 304

Puzzle 21

Which of the constructed boxes cannot be made from the pattern?

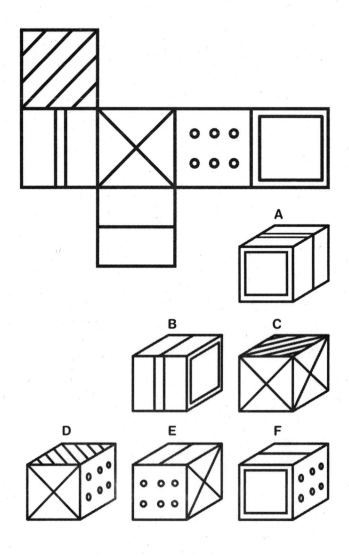

A

B   C

D   E   F

Answer see page 305

Puzzle 22

There is only one way to open this safe. You must press each button once only, in the correct order, to reach OPEN. Each button is marked with a direction, U for up, L for left, D for down, R for right. The number of spaces to move is also marked on each button. Which button must you press first to open the safe?

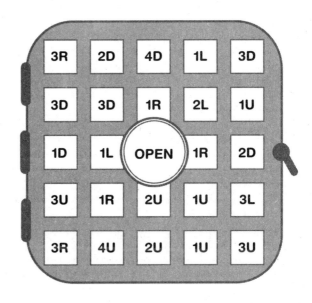

Puzzle 23

SEEDS

~DEEDS SLEDS~

~DEARS SLEW~

~BEANS SLOWS~

~BEANS GLOWS~

~GROWS~

~BRASS GROSS~

GRASS

Complete the word ladder by changing one letter of each word per step. The newly created word must be found in the dictionary. What are the words to turn seeds in to grass?

Answers see page 305

Puzzle 24

Discover the connection between the letters and the numbers. Which number should replace the question mark?

G	7
M	13
U	21
J	10
W	?

14	23	9
A	**B**	**C**

26	2	11
D	**E**	**F**

Puzzle 25

Which letters, based on the alphanumeric system, should go into the blank boxes?

6	1	7	3					5	1	3	9					2	2	9	2			
1	3	5	4	A	H	B		2	8	6	4	F	B	C		4	3	0	9			
7	7	0	9					8	6	2	6					7	1	7	8			

Answers see page 305-6

Puzzle 26

Which two patterns do not go with the other three?

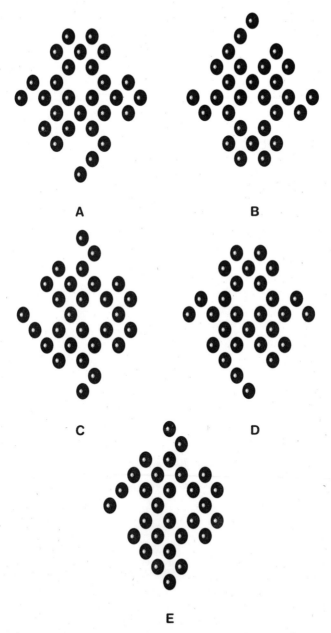

A

B

C

D

E

Answer see page 306

Puzzle 27

Which of the following is the odd one out?

A. CUBE

B. SQUARE

C. SPHERE

D. CYLINDER

E. OCTAHEDRON

Puzzle 28

Can you figure out what comes next ?

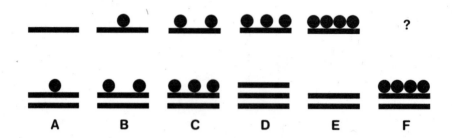

Answers see page 306

Puzzle 29 – Sudoku

		6		5			8	
	5		2			6		
						9	2	5
1	9		7			3		8
7		5	9					
4	6		5			2		7
						7	3	4
	4		6			8		
		8		2			6	

Puzzle 30

Look at the five figures. Which of the following options continues the sequence?

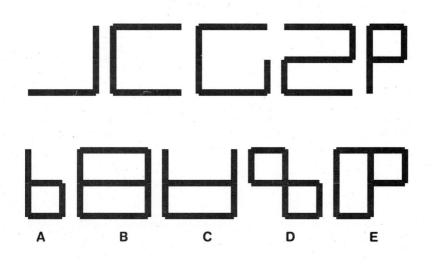

A   B   C   D   E

Answers see page 307

Puzzle 31

Which of the segments below is missing from the diagram above?

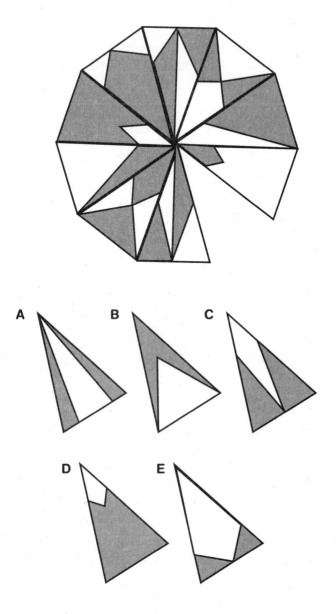

Answer see page 307

Puzzle 32

Change the second letter of each word to the left and to the right. Two other English words must be formed. Place the letter used in the empty section. When this has been completed, for all the words, another English word can be read down.

What is the word?

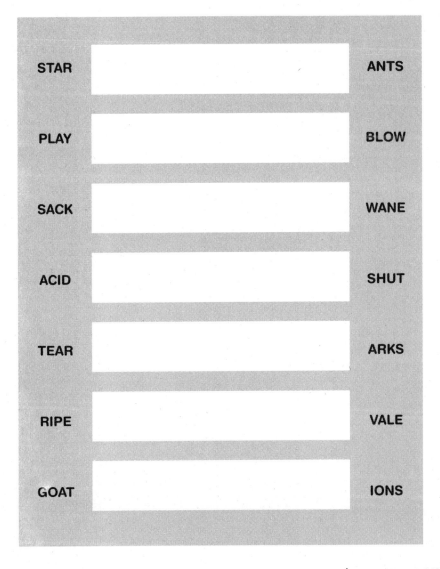

STAR		ANTS
PLAY		BLOW
SACK		WANE
ACID		SHUT
TEAR		ARKS
RIPE		VALE
GOAT		IONS

Answer see page 307

Puzzle 33

Find the eight places where the routes meet to form crossroads rather than crossovers.

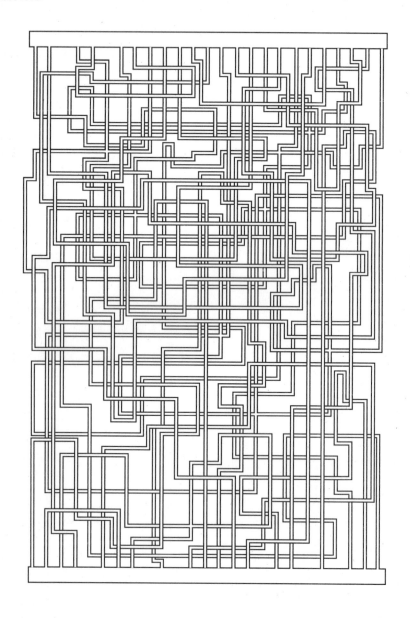

Answer see page 308

Puzzle 34

At the school the boys sit at desks numbered 1–5 and the girls sit opposite them at desks numbered 6–10.

1. The girl sitting next to the girl opposite no. 1 is Fiona.
2. Fiona is three desks away from Grace.
3. Hilary is opposite Colin.
4. Eddy is opposite the girl next to Hilary.
5. If Colin is not central then Alan is.
6. David is next to Bill.
7. Bill is three desks away from Colin.
8. If Fiona is not central then Indira is.
9. Hilary is three desks away from Jane.
10. David is opposite Grace.
11. The girl sitting next to the girl opposite Alan is Jane.
12 Colin is not at desk no. 5.
13. Jane is not at desk no. 10.

Eddy X Hilary

Can you work out the seating arrangements?

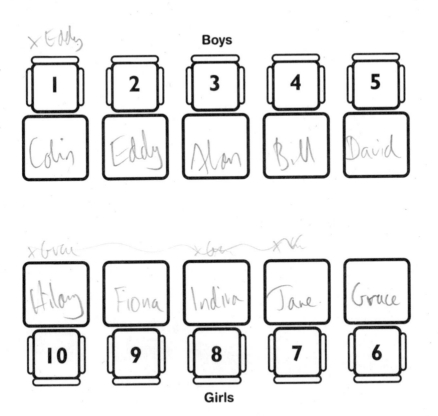

Boys

| 1 | 2 | 3 | 4 | 5 |

| Colin | Eddy | Alan | Bill | David |

| Hilary | Fiona | Indira | Jane | Grace |

| 10 | 9 | 8 | 7 | 6 |

Girls

Answer see page 309

Puzzle 35

Replace the vowels in each of the following to form words. Which words are the odd ones out?

A.

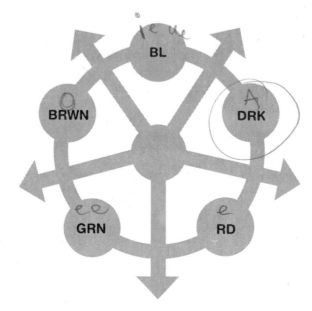

B.

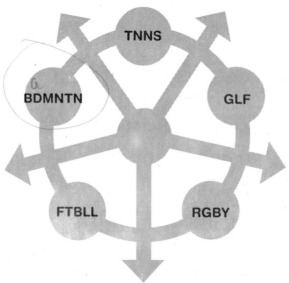

Answer see page 309

Puzzle 36

What word is opposite in meaning to EVASIVE?

A. ZEALOUS

B. EXACT

C. OPEN

D. CAUSTIC

E. BRAVE

Puzzle 37 – Sudoku

			4			7	9	
		9		5	7			6
	2							1
				2			3	
		4			3		1	
	1		9					8
				3			5	
5	4		1			2		
	9							

Answers see page 309

Puzzle 38

Find a route from the top of this puzzle to the bottom that arrives at the total 353, always going down and to an adjoining hexagon.

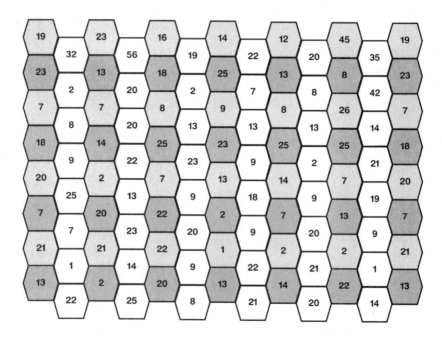

Answer see page 310

Puzzle 39

When rearranged the shapes will give a number. Which of the numbers is it?

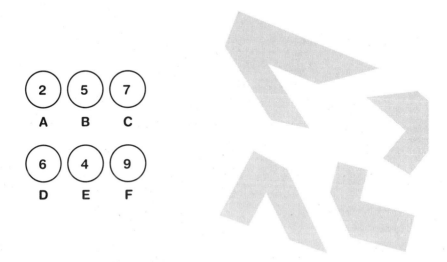

(2) (5) (7)
 A   B   C

(6) (4) (9)
 D   E   F

Puzzle 40

Can you work out how many regular hexagons are in this collection?

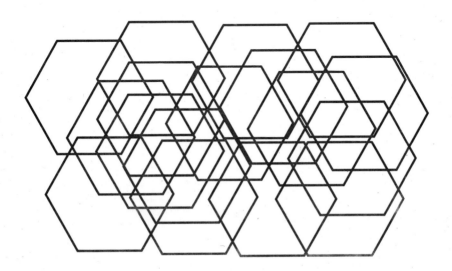

Answers see page 310

Puzzle 41

Can you re-assemble these blocks of three into the blanks to form a magic square in which the numbers in each row, column and long diagonal add to 175 ?

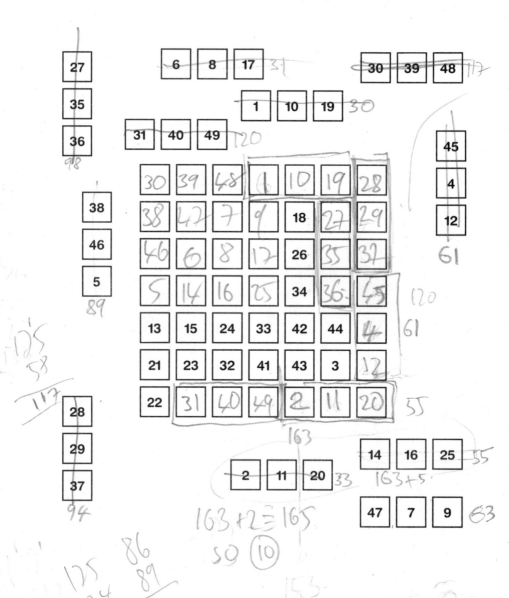

Puzzle 42

The wordframe, when filled with the correct letters will give the name of a city in England and Alabama. The letters are arranged in the coded square. There are two possible letters to fill each square of the wordframe, one correct, one incorrect.

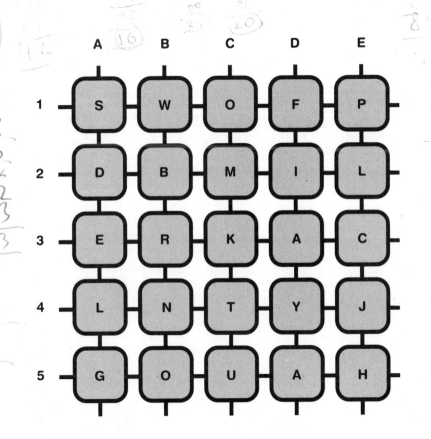

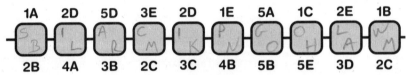

1A	2D	5D	3E	2D	1E	5A	1C	2E	1B
2B	4A	3B	2C	3C	4B	5B	5E	3D	2C

Answer see page 311

41

Puzzle 43 – Sudoku

	9		5					
4							7	
			7	3			1	
		4	2		8			
		5	6	4		8		
				9	5	4		1
		1		8	6			
	7							5
6							2	

Puzzle 44

Place the letters shown into the diagram in such a way that three words can be read across and one down the middle. What are the words?

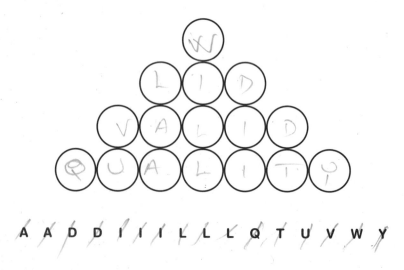

A A D D I I I L L L Q T U V W Y

Answers see page 311

Puzzle 45

Each line and symbol in the four outer circles is transferred to the middle circle according to a few rules. These are that if a line or symbol occurs in the outer circles: once, it is transferred; twice, it is possibly transferred; three times, it is transferred; four times, it is not transferred.

Which of the five circles should appear in the middle of the diagram above?

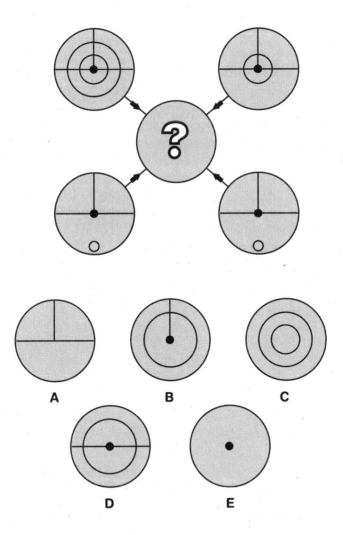

Answer see page 312

Puzzle 46

What is the answer if, from the number below, you multiply by five the number of even numbers that are immediately followed by an odd number?

4 7 8 5 3 1 9 7 8 4 4 7 8 9 2 3

Puzzle 47

Three little boys who were comparing their allowance money found that each of them had only one type of coin in his pocket.

The first had his money all in five-cent coins, the second had all ten-cent coins, and the third had only fifty-cent coins.

The boys thought that it would only be fair if they had equal amounts of money. Mental arithmetic was not their strongest subject. so they started exchanging coins, recounting after each exchange.

After some time they eventually ended up with $1.80 each, and found that each boy had given two of his original coins to each of the other two boys.

How many of each type of conis did the boys have to begin with?

Answers see page 312

Puzzle 48

What would this pyramid look like opened out?

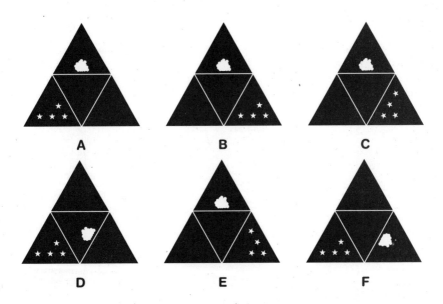

Answer see page 312

Puzzle 49

Can you solve the following anagrams to find the names of eight countries ?

VISUAL YOGA

AS A RITUAL

COLD ANTS

SIR USA

OUR HANDS

A FRUIT CHAOS

GREY MAN

BAD BOARS

Puzzle 50 – Sudoku

	7	4	6			9		
5								
	2		4		3			
		8	2		1	5	6	
7	1		8	3			2	
		5	9		7	8	3	
	6		5		4			
3								
	5	2	3			6		

Answers see page 313

Puzzle 51

This square follows a logical pattern. Which of the tiles should be used to complete the square?

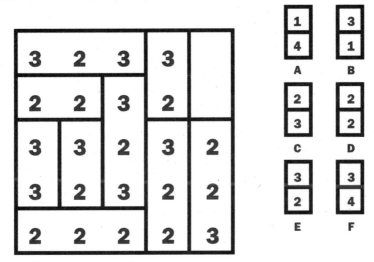

Puzzle 52

Marianne lived alone in a big house. She rarely left her house and spent most of her time maintaining the property, reading classical literature, and listening to music. One evening she ran out of food and decided to go to the 24 hour shop for some more. Upon leaving, she turned off the TV & lights. She was away for a couple of hours, but to her horror, when she got back she found that she was responsible for the deaths of eighty people.

What happened to them?

Answers see page 313

Puzzle 53

This clock has been designed for a planet that rotates on its axis once every 16 hours. There are 64 minutes to every hour, and 64 seconds to the minute. At the moment, the time on the clock reads a quarter to eight. What time, to the nearest second, will the clock say the time after the next time the hands appear to meet?

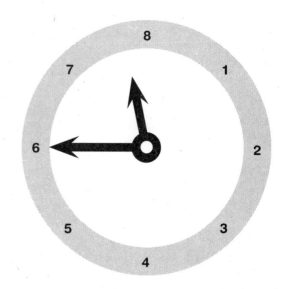

Puzzle 54

I have recently collected data on the changes of weather where I live, and have arrived at the following possibilities for the month of June. If it is fine today, the probability that it will be fine tomorrow is 3/4. If it is wet today, the probability that it will be fine tomorrow is 1/3. Today is Thursday, and the weather is warm and sunny. I plan to go walking on Sunday.

What is the probability that Sunday will be a fine day?

Answers see page 314

Puzzle 55

What number should replace the question mark?

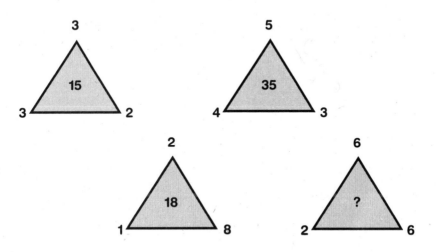

Puzzle 56

PLEAD   LABEL   ALBUM   LUSTY?

What word continues the above sequence?

A. FROWN

B. UTTER

C. LUNCH

D. DREAM

E. CHARM

Answers see page 314

Puzzle 57

A new repairer starts work repairing telephones. There are 15 booths in his area. The supervisor tells him that five out of the first eight booths need repairing and that he should go and repair one as a test.

The man goes straight to booth number eight. Why?

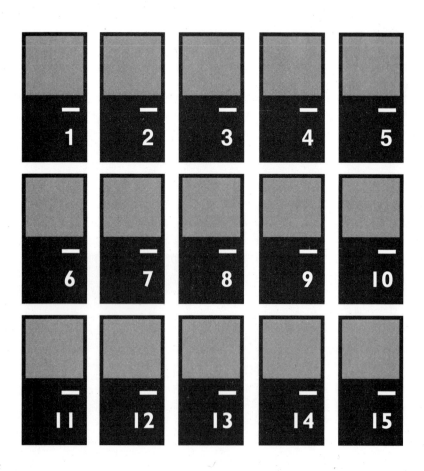

Answer see page 315

Puzzle 58 – Sudoku

	3			7		8	5	
9	8		2			3		
				6	3	4		1
				2		7	1	
	4	7		3				
3		1	7	4				
		2			1		6	3
	5	8		9			4	

Puzzle 59 – Sudoku

6						1		8
3				8	4		2	
				9				4
		2		1		9		
		6	2		9	3		
		5		4		7		
8				5				
	5		9	6				3
9		4						5

Answers see page 315

Puzzle 60 – Shape Sudoku

As with "classic" Sudoku, each row and column must contain the numbers 1 to 9 once only – and so must each shape within the grid.

Puzzle 61 – Shape Sudoku

Answers see page 315-6

Puzzle 62 – Killer Sudoku

As with "classic" Sudoku, each row and column must contain the numbers 1 to 9 once only – and within each cell marked with dotted lines the digits must sum to the given number.

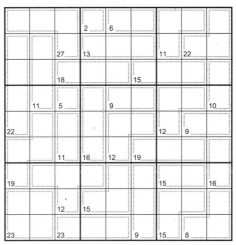

Puzzle 63 – Greater Than Sudoku

As with "classic" Sudoku, each row and column must contain the numbers 1 to 9 once only. The shapes created by the cells depict a greater than (>) or less than (<) symbol, showing that the value in a cell is larger or smaller than its neighbour.

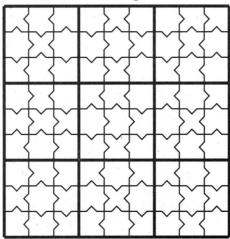

Answers see page 316

Puzzle 64 – Samurai Sudoku

As with "classic" Sudoku, each row and column must contain the numbers 1 to 9 once only. However, there are five puzzles: there's a central grid to complete as well as an extra one connected to each of the four corners.

Answer see page 316

Puzzle 65

As park ranger on this safari you have to collect as many rattlesnakes as possible without the risk of getting killed or maimed by the other creatures. The bears and wildcats have marked one segment next to the one they stand on, but you have no way of knowing which one, so you may not pass over or next to one. You may not go back over your tracks. Start on the shaded sector and finish on the snake facing to the left.

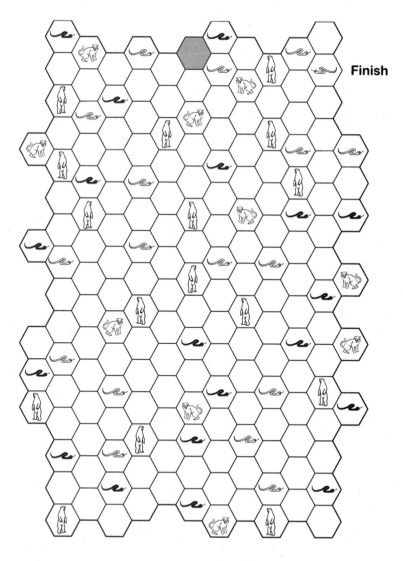

Finish

Answer see page 317

Puzzle 66

Start at any corner and follow the lines. Collect another four numbers and total the five. One of the numbers in the squares below can be used to complete the diagram. If the correct one has been chosen, one of the routes involving it will give a total of 28. Which one is it?

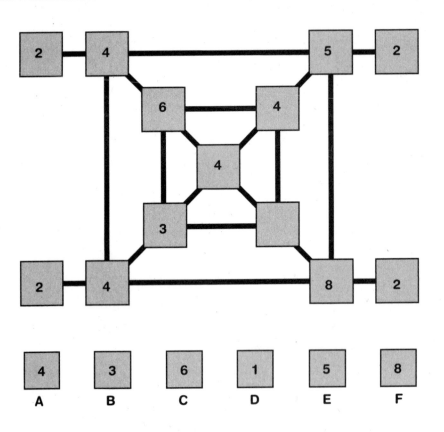

Puzzle 67

How many different ways is it possible to arrange the order of these four kings?

Answer see page 317

Puzzle 68

Arrange the pieces to form a square where the numbers read the same horizontally and vertically. What will the finished square look like?

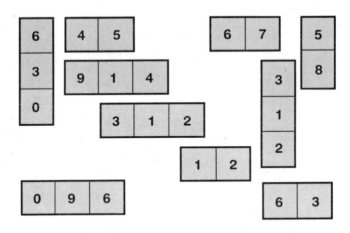

Puzzle 69

Start at the bottom letter M and move from circle to touching circle to the N at the top right. How many different ways are there of collecting the nine letters of MANHATTAN?

Answers see page 317-8

Puzzle 70

Look at the three hexagons. Which of the following four options continues the sequence?

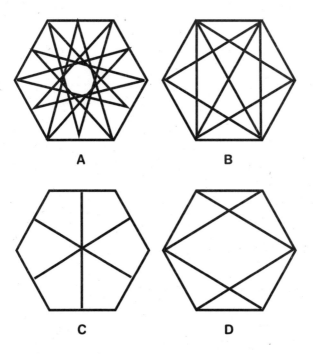

A

B

C

D

Answers see page 318

Puzzle 71

What would this pyramid look like opened out?

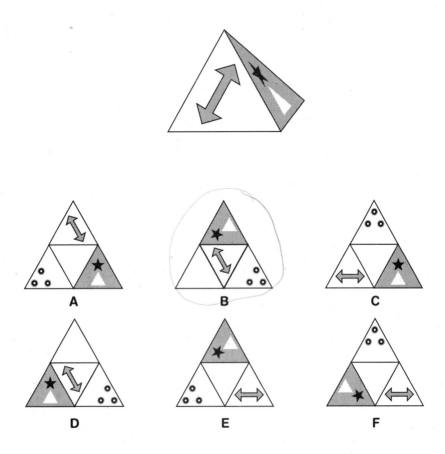

Puzzle 72

This is an unusual safe. To open it you must press the OPEN button, but you must press all the other buttons in the correct order. This can only be done by following the directions and the number of steps to be taken. Which is the first button you should push?

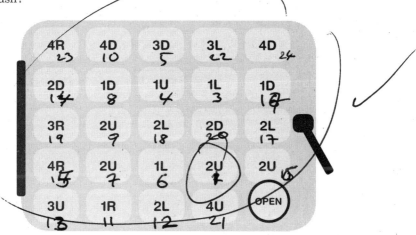

4R	4D	3D	3L	4D
2D	1D	1U	1L	1D
3R	2U	2L	2D	2L
4R	2U	1L	2U	2U
3U	1R	2L	4U	OPEN

Puzzle 73 – Sudoku

6	3	2	4	9	5	7	1	8
8	7	4	3	2	1	5	6	9
9	5	1	7	6	8	2	3	4
7	2	3	9	5	2	8	4	1
4	8	6	1	3	6	9	7	5
5	1	9	8	4	7	6	2	3
2	6	8	5	1	3	4	9	7
3	9	7	6	8	4	1	5	2
1	4	5	2	7	9	3	8	6

Answers see page 318-9

Puzzle 74

Which two of these form an identical pair that do not go with the other eight?

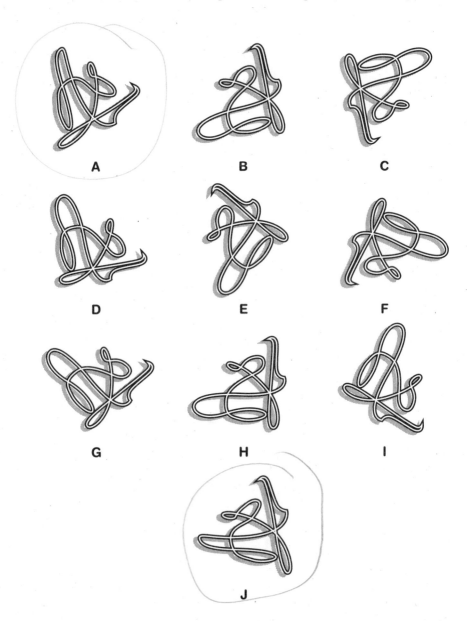

Answer see page 319

Puzzle 75

This grid contains three sports all spelled in the correct order, but mixed with the other two. Which are they?

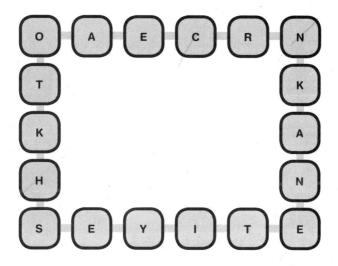

Puzzle 76

Find a six-letter word made up of only the following four letters.

G M
N O

Answers see page 319

Puzzle 77

Select one letter from each of the segments. When the correct letters have been found a word of eight letters can be read clockwise. What is the word?

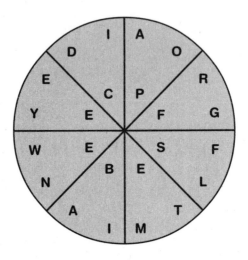

Puzzle 78

Which of the numbers should logically replace the question mark in the octagon?

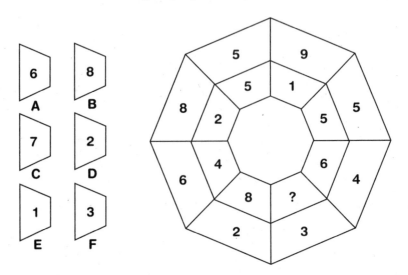

Answers see page 320

Puzzle 79

From the information given, work out the missing total and the values of the different images.

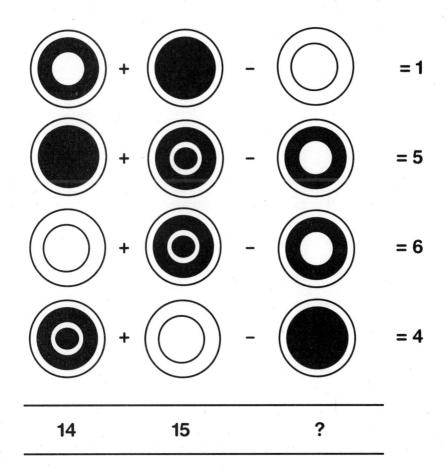

Answer see page 320

Puzzle 80

Four suspects – Jack Vicious, Sid Shifty, Alf Muggins and Jim Pouncer – are being interviewed at the scene of a murder. Each of the suspects is asked a question. Their answers are as follows:

Jack Vicious: "Sid Shifty committed the murder."

Sid Shifty: "Jim Pouncer committed the murder."

Alf Muggins: "I didn't commit the murder."

Jim Pouncer: "Sid Shifty is lying."

Only one of the four answers is the truth. Who committed the murder?

Puzzle 81 – Sudoku

	7	4						
2	5		6		4		3	
9		8						7
	9			4		7		5
			3				8	
	6							
			2			3		
	1			5			7	
		6	9					2

Answers see page 320-1

Puzzle 82 – Sudoku

						3		
8								4
	1	3	8				2	
4					5			3
3	9		2		7			
6					8			5
	8	2	7				4	
5								8
						6		

Puzzle 83

Place an English word of THREE letters in the empty space. This word, when added to the end of the three words to the left and to the beginning of the three words on the right, will form six other words. What is the word?

RED		OUNCE
BID		TIN
HID		TIL

Answers see page 321

Puzzle 84

In the grid you can find all the American States listed below.

Alaska	Arizona
California	Colorado
Montana	Nevada
New Mexico	Oregon
Texas	Wyoming

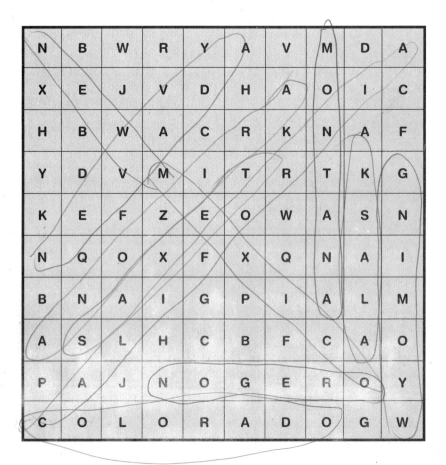

Answer see page 321

Puzzle 85

In the English countryside is a traditional manor house. Five staff work there, each of whom has a different hobby and a different rest day.

1. The man who has Tuesday off plays golf but is not the janitor, who is called Clark.
2. Jones is not the butler who plays squash.
3. Wood has Wednesday off and is not the butler or the gardener.
4. James is the cook and does not have Thursdays off; Smith also does not have Thursdays off (or Tuesdays, either).
5. Bridge is played on Monday; the chauffeur does not play chess; and James does not have Tuesdays off.

What are their names, how is each employed, what is the pastime of each, and on which day of the week does each have a rest day?

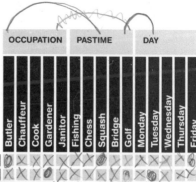

Name	Occupation	Pastime	Rest Day
James	Cook	Bridge	Monday
Clark	Janitor	Chess	Thursday
Wood	Chauffeur	Fishing	Wednesday
Smith	Butler	Squash	Friday
Jones	Gardener	Golf	Tuesday

Answer see page 322

Puzzle 86

Discover the connection between the letters and the numbers. Which numbers should go in the empty box?

C	3	14	N
Y	25	12	L
F	6	19	S
U	21	16	P
O	15	4	D

15	4

A

5	26

B

11	18

C

24	8

D

13	3

E

1	19

F

Answer see page 322

Puzzle Mix 2

Puzzle 1

Five of the words in the diagram are associated for some reason. Find the words and then work out whether PLANT belongs to the group.

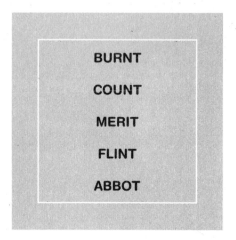
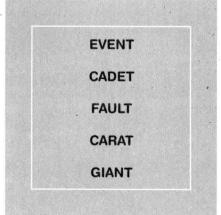

BURNT	EVENT
COUNT	CADET
MERIT	FAULT
FLINT	CARAT
ABBOT	GIANT

Puzzle 2

Place two of the three-letter segments together to make a six-letter bug.

ANT   BEE   SCA   TLY   RAB   FLY

Answers see page 323

Puzzle 3

A jailer has a large number of prisoners to guard and has to seat them at a number of tables at mealtimes. The regulations state the following seating arrangements:

1. Each table is to seat the same number of prisoners.
2. The number at each table is to be an odd number.

The jailer finds that when he seats the prisoners:

3 per table, he has 2 prisoners left over;
5 per table, he has 4 prisoners left over;
7 per table, he has 6 prisoners left over;
9 per table, he has 8 prisoners left over;

but when he seats them 11 per table there are none left over.

How many prisoners are there?

Puzzle 4 – Sudoku

3	8	5	2		6	7	4	9
1	4	6	3	7	9	2	8	5
2	7	9	4	8	5	3	1	6
8	3	1	7	6	2	5	9	4
4	6	2	9	5	3	1	7	8
9	5	7	8	4	1	6	2	3
7	1	3	5	9	4	8	6	2
6	2	4	1	3	8	9	5	7
5	9	8	6	2	7	4	3	1

Answers see page 323

Puzzle 5

This is an unusual maze. There are a few ways of completing it, but the aim is to collect as few points as possible. What is the lowest possible score?

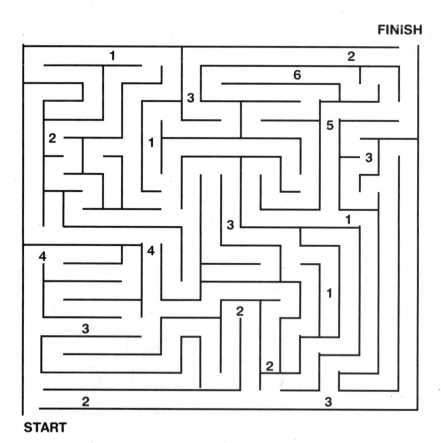

Answers see page 324

Puzzle 6

When rearranged the shapes will give a number. Which of the numbers is it?

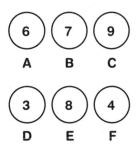

Puzzle 7

Two words using the same letters in their construction can be used to replace the dots in this sentence. The sentence will then make sense. Each dot is one letter. What are the words?

> AFTER THE DOUBLE WEDDING, THE
>
> TWO • • • • • • WALKED THROUGH THE HALL,
>
> WHICH WAS LITTERED WITH THE • • • • • •
>
> FROM THE PARTY HELD THE PREVIOUS NIGHT.

Answers see page 324

Puzzle 8

Which of the surrounding pieces fits perfectly on top of the middle piece to make a rectangular block?

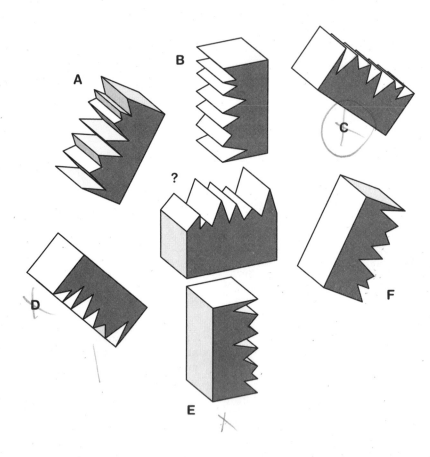

Answer see page 324

Puzzle 9 – Sudoku

2						8	7	
	8		2				9	
				5		1		
	1		5		9		2	
		8			1			3
			3	2				
6		5						
3	7		1				8	
				7				9

CHOP

TREE

Puzzle 10

Complete the word ladder by changing one letter of each word per step. The newly created word must be found in the dictionary.

What are the words to turn CHOP into TREE?

Answers see page 325

Puzzle 11

A quotation has been written in this diagram. Find the start letter and move from square to touching square until you have found it.

What is the quotation and to whom is it attributed?

E	H	O	P	E	K	T	T
N	T	C	U	E	A	H	D
I	K	T	I	E	H	E	N
E	O	F	Y	U	A	T	A
H	T	F	O	C	N	T	S

Answer see page 325

Puzzle 12

On the far eastern side of the Algarve, close to the Spanish border, is a town whose roads are laid out in grid fashion, like Manhattan. This system was first used in the cities of Ancient Greece. Seven friends live at different corners, marked ○. They wish to meet for coffee.

On which corner should they meet in order to minimize the walking distance for all seven?

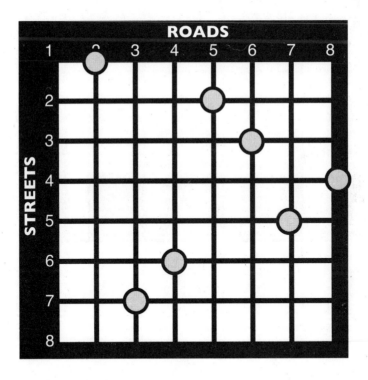

Answer see page 325

Puzzle 13

Complete the square using the five symbols shown. When completed no row, column or diagonal line will use the same symbol more than once. What should replace the question mark?

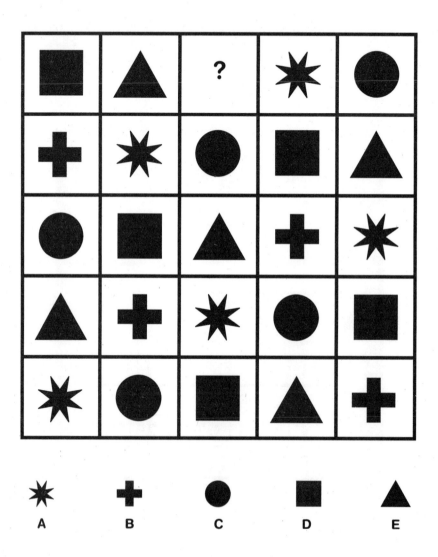

Answer see page 326

Puzzle 14

What should replace the question mark?

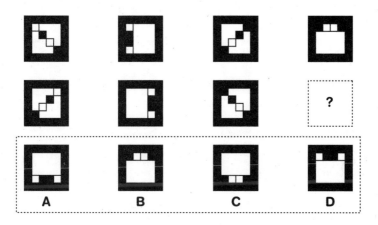

Puzzle 15 – Sudoku

			2	4	1			
2	5					7		
	1							8
	9	3	6					
5			8			2		
	2	6	4					
	6							5
7	3					8		
			3	6	9			

Answers see page 326

Puzzle 16

CUT PERM
is an anagram of what seven-letter word?

Puzzle 17

Anastasia has thought of a number between 99 and 999. Belinda asks whether the number is below 500; Anastasia answers yes. Belinda asks whether the number is a square number; Anastasia answers yes. Belinda asks whether the number is a cube number; Anastasia answers yes. However, Anastasia has told the truth to only two of the three questions. Anastasia then tells Belinda truthfully that both the first and the last digit are 5, 7 or 9.

What is the number?

Puzzle 18 – Sudoku

	1		5	3		4	9	5 7
4	3	6	6	7	1	5	8	2
			9	4		3	6	1
		3	1	5		8	2	4
8			3	2		1	57	9
	2	1	4	8		6	52	3
5	8	2	7	1	3	9	4	6
1	9	9	2	6	5	7	3	8
3	6	7	8	9	4	2	1	5

Puzzle 19

In this grid, the ten words related to things that are useful to have for puzzle solving may go up, down, along, backwards or forwards, or diagonally, but they all have at least one bend somewhere.

Can you find the following ten words in the grid ?

INTELLIGENCE
THINKING
HEAD
IMAGINATION
MEMORY

CLARITY
PLANNING
INTROSPECTION
CREATIVITY
FORESIGHT

Answer see page 327

Puzzle 20

This is a two part puzzle.

a. Can you find the following words in the grid below ? :

BELLS; FISHES; BEES; SLEEP; BIRDS; BONES; DREAMS; EGGS; FIRE.

b. Can you link each of the words you find with its appropriate `ology' from the following list ?

OSTEOLOGY; HYPNOLOGY; CAMPANOLOGY; ICHTHYOLOGY; PYROLOGY; APIOLOGY; ORNITHOLOGY; OOLOGY; ONEIRILOGY.

Words may appear written in any direction.

Z	R	O	N	M	P	D	R	E	A	M	S	O	O	L	K	I
P	G	J	K	V	J	K	N	L	K	Z	H	G	H	J	K	O
A	L	R	B	O	C	J	I	O	P	R	A	B	L	A	I	M
T	R	I	D	E	W	A	S	T	A	B	L	A	N	R	I	N
N	O	N	S	E	L	N	N	S	E	W	U	R	D	Z	A	E
I	M	P	E	L	S	L	P	E	O	P	B	C	R	T	R	R
T	R	A	K	B	E	M	S	E	K	A	I	M	E	M	T	I
C	L	E	S	T	F	R	O	F	A	C	R	P	R	P	C	F
A	N	E	R	I	S	E	N	U	D	O	D	O	M	I	C	L
Q	U	E	S	V	O	V	A	I	M	N	S	T	H	I	B	R
E	G	H	A	M	C	P	L	U	N	D	T	O	O	B	Y	N
R	E	I	L	L	I	N	E	R	G	A	N	D	O	Y	P	O
S	L	H	I	V	E	R	S	E	O	F	G	N	U	N	G	E
E	L	U	O	E	T	T	S	O	L	O	E	E	O	F	A	L
A	H	P	N	E	N	O	O	P	E	S	T	L	H	E	P	O
K	H	G	A	B	T	V	H	L	E	G	G	O	A	M	V	E
S	T	R	E	G	G	S	O	O	M	W	A	N	N	T	I	R

Puzzle 21

In this grid the word 'POTATO', written without a change of direction, appears only once. It can be written forwards or backwards in a horizontal, vertical or diagonal direction. Can you spot it?

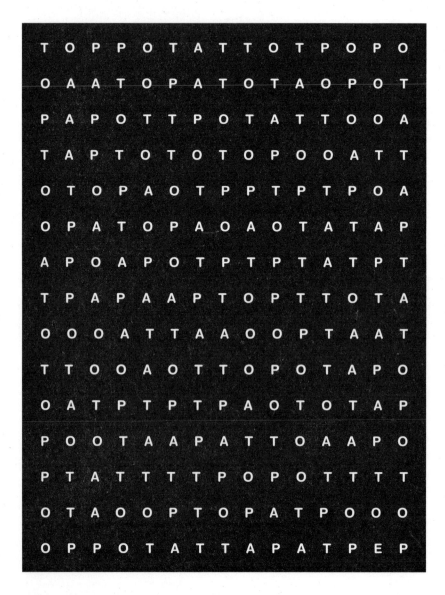

Answer see page 328

Puzzle 22

In this grid are hidden the names of 18 famous authors. Can you detect them? You can go forward or in reverse, in horizontal, vertical and diagonal lines.

Austen	**Chekhov**	**Flaubert**
Hemingway	**Ibsen**	**Kipling**
Michener	**Proust**	**Twain**
Chaucer	**Dickens**	**Goethe**
Huxley	**Kafka**	**Lawrence**
Orwell	**Tolstoy**	**Zola**

```
C W C O A L M K W O E A C K L G O Z A N
L H H E M I N G W A Y E I Y L M O X A E
L E E C M O X K W A X F E X A N B K O S
C F A K K E N Z A E X L A E B L P E F B
A Y E L H M Z N O E X I A I F H R K L I
M O Q V T O A T E U I W E H T E O G M O
A T K V L A V C H A E M N O L E U A B C
F S I A T A M Q L S D I C K E N S S T A
A L S T V E M W M N O E I A C H T A C T
F O O X W A B E A L L E I T A W W A C G
G T O X A E A K F A K I L A A S T A W N
O N F B C H J K W L L T J I I E X G H I
E N O L F M G O Z X A Y N A E B E C W L
R V O L F I G A E Z I U I E J C C K T P
E W U V E C U O P T E G B P N H T S E I
C S E W X H L H J A L E C E K L T U Z K
U A T A E E C K U W P Q R A R A E P A Z
A U S T E N X A T A Q W A L E T A W V E
H A P E X E A B C B A C A E W W E X L E
C C W A O R W E L L K M N O P P E L T U
```

Answer see page 328

Puzzle 23

Five pairs of husband and wife aliens arrive for the intergalactic meeting on Earth. For ease of recognition, the males are known by the letter M followed by an odd number and the females by F and an even number. Each pair has different distinguishing features and has prepared a different subject for discussion. They arrive in different types of spacecraft and dock in a set of five bays. The pairs sit in five double seats in the auditorium.

1. M1 is preparing his speech on time travel and has arrived in a warp distorter.

2. The mind-reading couple who have four arms each have parked their nebula accelerator between the space oscillator and the astro carrier.

3. F6, in the pair of seats next to the left-end pair, says to the alien next to her, "My husband M3 and I have noticed that you have three legs."

4. F4 admires the galaxy freighter owned by the pair who each have three eyes, who are in the next seats.

5. The husband of F8 is turning his papers on time travel with 12 fingers.

6. M5, in the middle pair of seats, says to F10 in the next pair of seats, "The pair with webbed feet on your other side have an astro carrier."

7. M7 and F2 are studying their papers on anti-gravity. The husband of F6 is studying his papers on nuclear fission.

Who is the wife of M9 and who is the male speaker on nuclear fission?

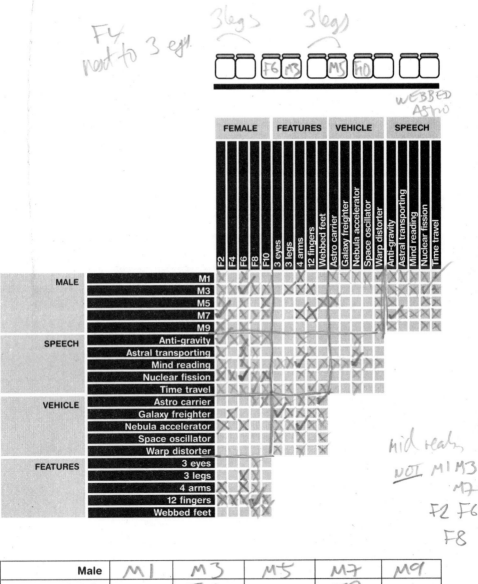

F4 next to 3 egg.

3 legs   *3 legs*

F6 M5   *M5 H0*

WEBBED Astro

Mid reads NOT M1 M3 M7 F2 F6 F8

Male	M1	M3	M5	M7	M9
Female		F6		F2	
Vehicle	Warp dist				
Speech	Time trvl	Nuclear		Anti-Grav	
Features					

NOT M1, M3 or M7.

4 arms
Nebula Accelator.
Mind reading.

Answer see page 328

Puzzle 24 – Sudoku

		6			2			8
9					6		1	
3			1	5	9			
2				1	8	6	3	5
	7				4	8		
						2		
	6	7						3
4	9	3		2				
	8				3	5	7	

Puzzle 25

Can you work out what letter needs to be inserted in the middle to form four dances by combining opposite segments?

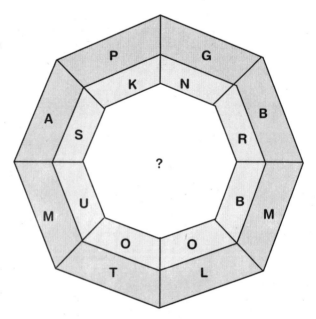

Answers see page 329

Puzzle 26

Previous to the time shown, when were all four of the digits on this watch last on display?

Puzzle 27

Which English word of four letters can be attached to the back of the words shown in the diagram to create six other words?

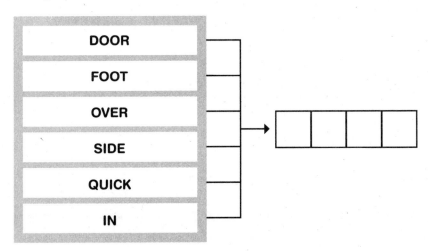

Answers see page 329

Puzzle 28

Here is an unusual safe. Each of the buttons must be pressed only once in the correct order to open it. The last button is marked F. The number of moves and the direction is marked on each button. Thus 1U would mean one move up, while 1L would mean one move to the left. Using the grid reference, which button is the first you must press?

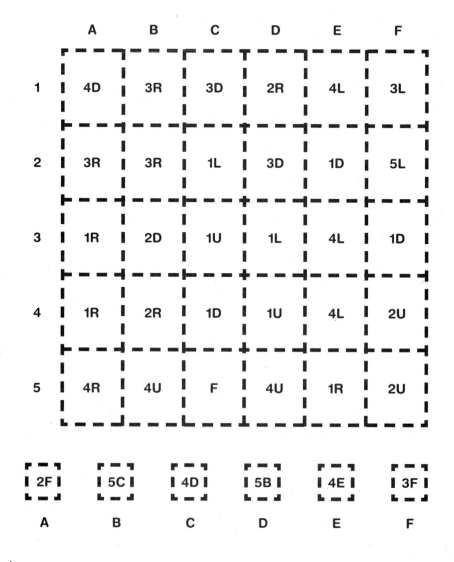

	A	B	C	D	E	F
1	4D	3R	3D	2R	4L	3L
2	3R	3R	1L	3D	1D	5L
3	1R	2D	1U	1L	4L	1D
4	1R	2R	1D	1U	4L	2U
5	4R	4U	F	4U	1R	2U

A	B	C	D	E	F
2F	5C	4D	5B	4E	3F

Answer see page 330

Puzzle 29

Look along each line and down each column of this shape. Which of the following eight options is the missing square?

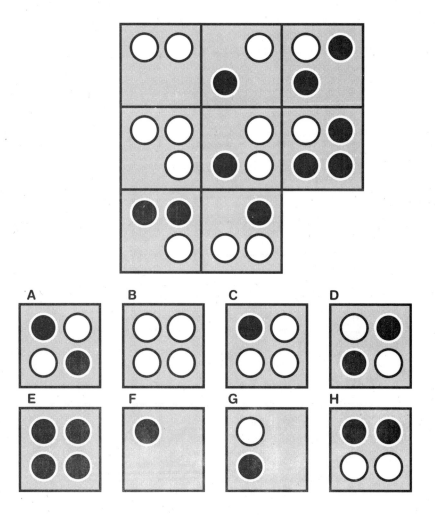

Answer see page 330

Puzzle 30

Don and Spencer are engaged by the local council to prune trees on either side of a tree-lined avenue. There is an equal number of trees on either side of the road. Don arrives first and has pruned three trees on the right-hand side when Spencer arrives and points out that Don should be pruning the trees on the left-hand side. So Don starts afresh on the left-hand side and Spencer continues on the right. When Spencer has finished his side he goes across the avenue and prunes six trees for Don, which finishes the job.

Who prunes the most trees and by how many?

Puzzle 31 – Sudoku

4	3	6	7	2	3	1	2	5
5		2	3	6	1	8		4
4		1	9	5	8	6	3	5
6	1	3	4	7	2	5	6	
6	5		1	9	3	4	6	2
23	23	4	5	8	6	9	1	2
2	4		6	3	9	7	5	1
1	2	5	8	4	7	3		6
2	6	8	1	5	7	4	

Puzzle 32

By taking a segment and finding its pair, the names of four books from the Old Testament can be made.

What are they?

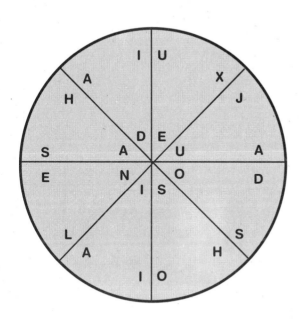

Puzzle 33

The names of four musical instruments can be found in the diagram. The letters are written in the correct order they normally appear.

What are the musical instruments?

D	I	I	O	N	O	U
T						A
N		C	C	H		N
O		A		O		I
M				A		M
U	R	B	A	R		P

Answers see page 331

Puzzle 34

Which of the constructed boxes can be made from the pattern?

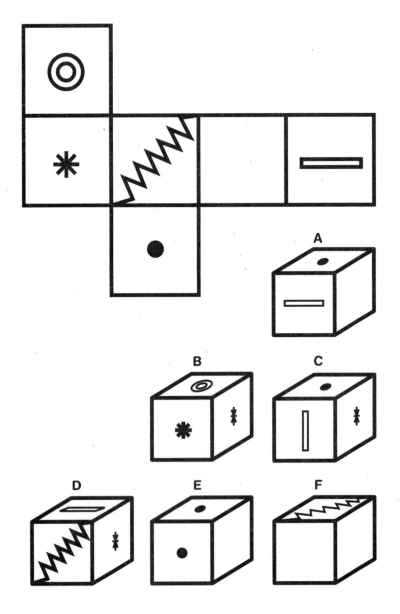

Puzzle 1

The word frame at the bottom is constructed from multi-tinted tiles. Choose a letter from the grid and insert it in the frame. The letter must be written on a matching tile. When the process has been completed a modern ruler's title can be found. What is it?

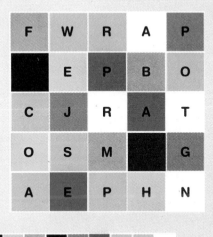

Puzzle 2

These objects can be arranged in a logical order in which the black square is first and the yellow hexagon is last. What is the order?

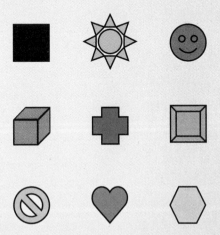

Answers see page 112

Puzzle 3

Which circle is missing
from the middle of
this series?

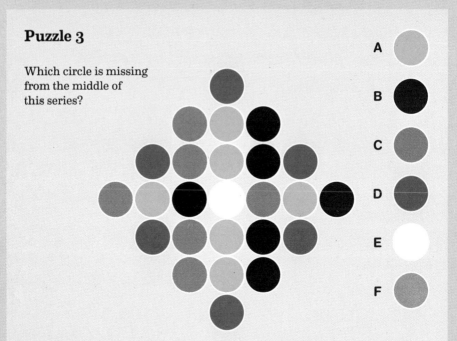

A

B

C

D

E

F

Puzzle 4

Which colour is the odd one out?

Answers see page 112

Puzzle 5

Find a number that could replace the question mark. Each colour represents a number under 10.

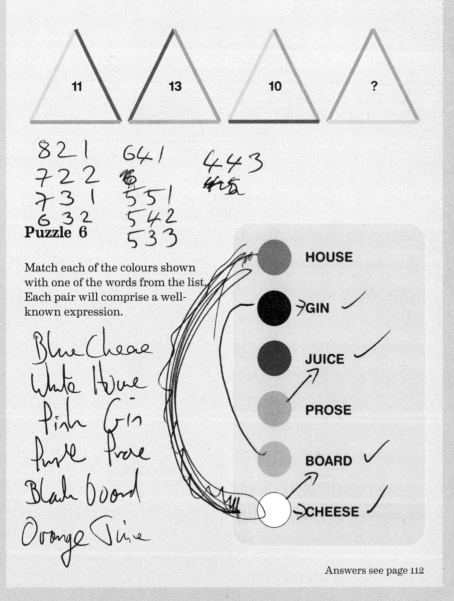

(handwritten working)

11   13   10   ?

821   641   443
722   ~~73~~   ~~442~~
731   551
632   542
533

Puzzle 6

Match each of the colours shown with one of the words from the list. Each pair will comprise a well-known expression.

(handwritten answers)
Blue Cheese
White House
Pink Gin
Purple Prose
Black Board
Orange Juice

HOUSE

GIN ✓

JUICE ✓

PROSE

BOARD ✓

CHEESE ✓

Answers see page 112

Puzzle 7

The two pictures are identical except for nine alterations made to the second version. See if you can spot the nine differences.

Answer see page 112

Puzzle 8

These coloured blocks can be rearranged to create a logical order. Red is still the first in the series and yellow the last. What is the order of the other colours?

Puzzle 9

Find a number that could replace the question mark. Each colour represents a number under 10.

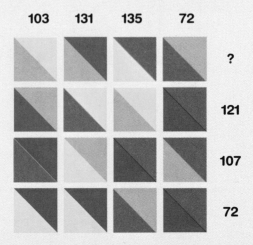

Answers see page 112

Puzzle 10

Find a number that could replace the question mark. Each colour represents a number under 10. Some may be negative numbers.

6	7	3	8	2	4	1	6	9	5	91
3	4	6	2	9	7	7	6	3	4	111
5	9	6	8	3	2	4	7			74
9	8	2	3			6	8			51
8	7	3	4			6	1	4	6	68
2	9	5	4	8	3	6	2	7	8	97
4	3	2	9	1	4	5	6	8	3	85
6	2	4	3	1	7	9	6	3	8	91
2	4	7	6			1	2			36
3	5	6	8			2	4			45
90	108	89	100	36	44	94	82	52	?	

Answer see page 112

103

Puzzle 11

Which square's contents matches A2?

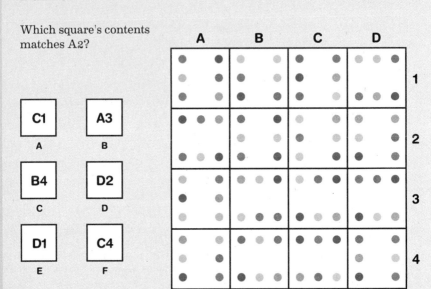

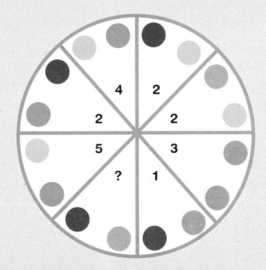

Puzzle 12

Find a number that could replace the question mark. Each colour represents a number under 10.

Answers see page 112

Puzzle 13

Should black go above or below the line?

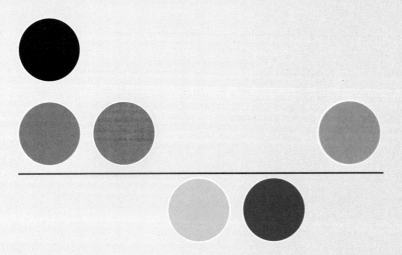

Puzzle 14

Can you crack the colour code and make your way from one red square to the other? Each colour takes you up, down, left or right. The blue arrow tells you which way is up.

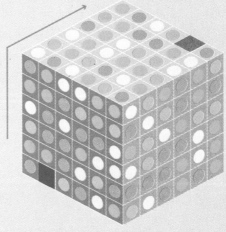

Answers see page 112

Puzzle 15

6	6	5	4	4	2
A	B	C	D	E	F

Here is an unusual safe. Each of the buttons must be pressed only once in the correct order to open it. The last button is marked F. The number of moves is marked on each button. A black number means move down. A red number means move up. A pink number means move left and a green number means move right. Thus a red 1 would mean one move up, whilst a green 1 would mean one move to the right. Which button is the first you must press?

F	5	1	3	3	5
5	4	2	1	3	1
1	2	2	1	2	1
1	1	3	1	3	1
2	3	2	2	1	1
4	2	3	1	4	1
2	2	1	2	1	6

Puzzle 16

Find a number that could replace the question mark. Each colour represents a number under 10.

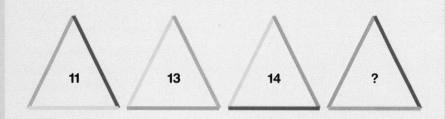

Answers see page 112

Puzzle 17

Move from circle to touching circle, starting from the bottom left corner and finishing in the top right corner. Collect nine circles each time. How many different routes are there to collect four orange, three blue, one pink and one green?

4	**7**	**2**
A	B	C
3	**5**	**4**
D	E	F

Puzzle 18

To find the missing number you need to discover the significance of the coloured shapes.

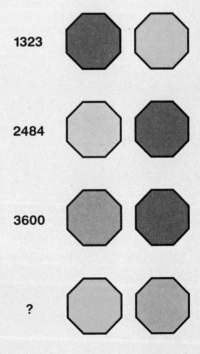

1323

2484

3600

?

Answers see page 112

Puzzle 19

Place the shape over the grid so that no colour appears twice in the same row or column. Beware, the shape may not be the right way up!

Puzzle 20

The colour of each square in pattern B is directly related to the colours in pattern A. The square colours in pattern C relate to pattern B the same way. Can you apply the same rules and fill in pattern D?

A   **B**   **C**   **D**

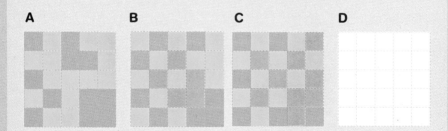

Answers see page 112

Puzzle 21

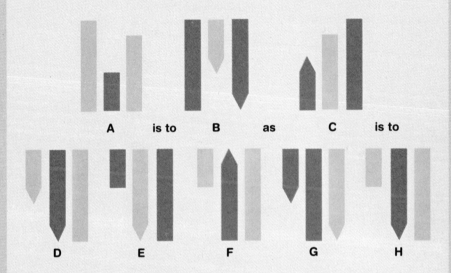

A   is to   B   as   C   is to

D   E   F   G   H

Puzzle 22

Which well known expression is represented by this rebus?

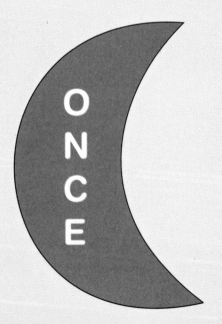

Answers see page 112

Puzzle 23

Find a number that could replace the question mark. Each colour represents a number under 10.

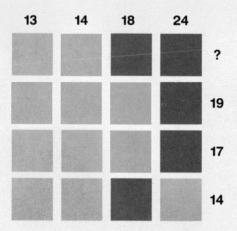

Puzzle 24

Which number replaces the question mark?

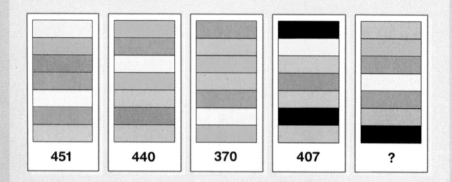

Answers see page 112

Puzzle 25

The letters can be rearranged to make a well-known Shakespearean phrase. The colours will help you.

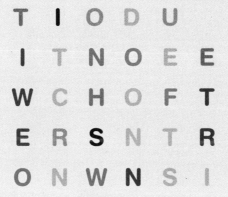

Puzzle 26

Which of the constructed boxes cannot be made from the pattern?

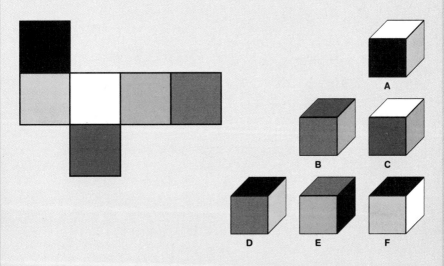

Answers see page 112

Solutions

1. Emperor of Japan.

2. Taking the colours in alphabetical order: black square, blue heart, brown cube, green crossed circle, orange square, pink sun, purple smiley, red cross, yellow hexagon.

3. D. Start at the top, the series reads red, blue, green, black and repeats from left to right.

4. Pink. All the other colors are either primary or secondary colors. Pink is a hue.

5. 14. Colours are worth: purple 2, yellow 3, orange 5, green 6. Add sides together and put sum in center of triangle.

6. Blue cheese, blackboard, purple prose, orange juice, pink gin, White House.

7.

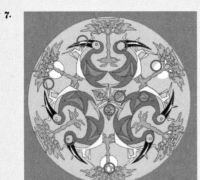

8. The correct order is based on the alphanumeric value of the words. It goes: red (27), blue (40), green (49), pink (50), orange (60), brown (72), purple (88), yellow (92).

9. 141. The colours are worth: red 2, green 4, orange 7, yellow 9. Multiply the numbers in each square together.

10. 54. The colours are worth: pink 3, orange 4, yellow 5, green 6, purple -2, red -4. Add the value of the colours to the number in each square.

11. F.

12. 2. The colours are worth: pink 1, green 2, orange 3, yellow 4, red 5, purple 6. In each segment subtract the smaller number from the larger and put the difference in the center of the next segment clockwise.

13. Above. Those above the line have only one syllable, those below have two.

14.

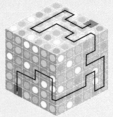

15. F. Pink 2 in the third row, third column.

16. 10. The colours are worth: orange 2, red 3, green 5, yellow 6. Add sides together and put sum in center of triangle.

17. B.

18. 2940. Multiply the alphanumeric equivalents of the pairs of colours.

19.

20.

When bordering squares (not diagonals) are predominantly green, a square becomes green. If they are predominantly yellow, it becomes yellow. If the bordering cell colours are equal in number, the square becomxes orange. If the bordering squares are predominantly orange, the square also becomes orange.

21. D.

22. Once in a blue moon.

23. 19. Colours are worth: purple 7, orange 3, red 5, green 4. Add colours in each row and column together.

24. 350 (based on alphanumeric values added).

25. 'Now is the winter of our discontent.' Letters of the same colour go together.

26. E.

Puzzle 35

The names of the following ten champagnes can be found in this grid on vertical, horizontal and diagonal lines. Can you find them?

Ayala
Bollinger
De Venoge
Deutz
Gosset

Henriot
Lanson
Pol Roger
Ruinart
Salon

D	G	J	B	F	H	C	L	G	B
D	E	U	T	Z	E	A	A	O	M
C	T	V	H	W	N	P	L	S	F
P	R	V	E	S	R	L	A	S	H
S	A	L	O	N	I	Q	Y	E	K
K	N	N	J	N	O	X	A	T	D
B	I	W	G	V	T	G	Q	B	W
D	U	E	Z	K	F	X	E	Y	G
F	R	E	G	O	R	L	O	P	Y
Q	G	X	V	C	H	X	Z	O	D

Answer see page 331

Puzzle 36

Complete the three-letter words which, reading down, will reveal a country.

T E (A) N A E

N I (L) B T L P

F O (G) R B E G

T I (E) C E K N P T

B A (R) D G N P R T Y

O B (I) E I

E R (A) A E

Algeria.

Puzzle 37 – Sudoku

	3	6	4				2	
	4	2						5
		1	2		8	3		4
	6		1	3				2
1	2	3	8	4				6
4			6	2	5		3	
6			5			2		
2						9		
3					2		1	

1
2
3
4
5
6
7
8
9

Answers see page 332

Puzzle 38

$$\frac{1}{6} \times 2Y$$

This system is balanced. How heavy is the box containing the question mark (ignoring leverage effects)?

$$13 + ? + 4X + 3x = \frac{Y}{3} + 4Y + 4x + 15.$$
$$+ \frac{5Y}{6} + 3Y \qquad ? \quad \frac{3Y}{6} + \frac{2624Y}{6\,6} + 4x + 15$$
$$\frac{5}{6}Y + \frac{18Y}{6} + 3x + 13 + ? = \frac{3Y}{6} + \frac{6}{6}\,6$$

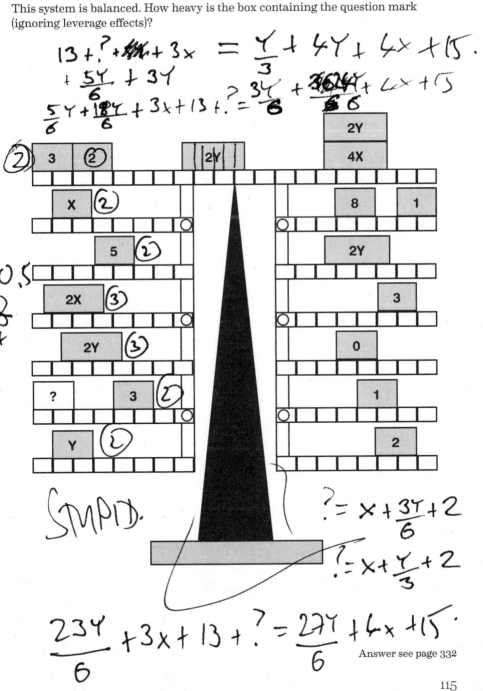

STUPID.

$$? = x + \frac{3Y}{6} + 2$$
$$? = x + \frac{Y}{3} + 2$$

$$\frac{23Y}{6} + 3x + 13 + ? = \frac{27Y}{6} + 4x + 15.$$

Answer see page 332

115

Puzzle 39

Which of the clocks continues this series?

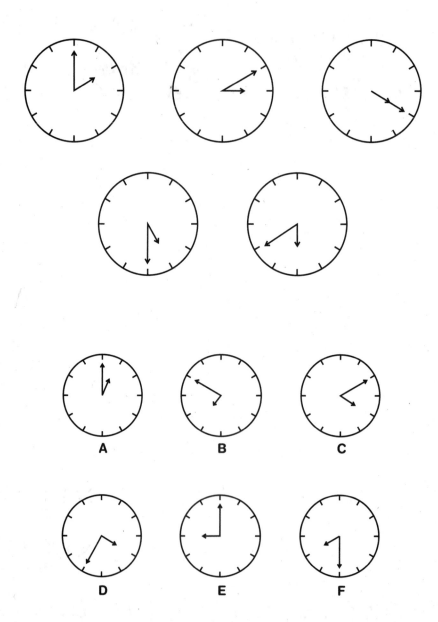

Answer see page 332

Puzzle 40

Local sports clubs take turns to plant a tree each year in the town's main street. A bird has established a nest in each tree.

1. The crow lives in the beech tree.

2. The lime was planted two years after the tree planted by the golf club.

3. The robin is in the tree planted by the bowling club, which is next to the tree planted by the soccer club.

4. Jim planted his tree in 1971.

5. The starling is in the poplar tree planted by Desmond in 1974.

6. Tony planted the middle tree – a beech.

7. Bill has an owl in his tree, which is next to the ash.

8. The tree at the right-hand end was planted in 1974 by the soccer club.

9. The elm was planted in 1970. ✓

10. The tennis club planted in 1972.

11. The squash club planted in 1970. ✓

12. Sylvester planted his tree in 1973 and it has a robin in it.

13. The blackbird is in the tree planted by Jim.

Work out which tree was planted by which member of each club and in which year.

Tree	BEECH	LIME	ELM	ASH	POPLAR
Person					
Club			SQUASH		
Bird	CROW				
Year			1970		

Answer see page 333

117

Puzzle 41

A knight, which moves either one square horizontally and two vertically or two horizontally and one vertically, starts at the shaded square of this small chess board visiting each square without returning to the same square twice. Find the route which spells out four famous cartoon characters.

I	R	P	I	O
B	C	G	E	A
E	L		Y	B
I	A	T	L	D
U	L	N	M	O

Puzzle 42 – Sudoku

	1		2		5			
4								
		5	3			8		6
5		9		6		7		
		8				5		
3					1		4	
		2	7	4			9	
					2	4		
		6						5

Answers see page 333

Puzzle Mix 3

Puzzle 1 – Sudoku

1	5	2	4	3	6	9	8	7
6	7	9	8	2	5	3	4	1
8	3	4	9	1	7	6	5	2
4	9	7	3	6	8	2	1	5
2	1	6	5	9	4	7	3	8
5	8	3	2	7	1	4	6	9
7	4	8	6	5	2	1	9	3
3	6	1	7	8	9	5	2	4
9	2	5	1	4	3	8	7	6

Puzzle 2

There are 189 members of the tennis club: 8 have been at the club less than three years; 11 are under 20 years of age; 70 wear spectacles; 140 are men.

What is the smallest number of players who had been members for three years or more, were at least 20 years of age, wore glasses and were men?

Answers see page 334

Puzzle 3

If the word Presidents is

☆ ❅ ❖ ✳ ☆ ♣ ❖ ❄ ✳ ❋
P R E S I D E N T S

Who are the other Presidents?

1. ✛ ❅ ☐ ▼ ❄ ☐
2. ❄ ✳ ▲ ❄ ■ ✳ ❏ ◗ ❄ ◻
3. ✳ ❏ ✳ ■ ▲ ❏ ■
4. ☐ ❄ ❅ ✳ ❄ ■
5. ◻ ❏ ❏ ▲ ❄ ❖ ❄ ● ▼

Puzzle 4

Select one of the two letters from the grid, in accordance with the reference shown, and place it in the word frame. When the correct letters have been chosen two linked words can be read. What are the words?

	A	B	C	D	E
1	O	I	N	V	M
2	E	S	I	R	B
3	R	T	U	B	C
4	W	A	S	M	H
5	E	T	I	N	S

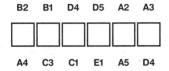

B2 B1 D4 D5 A2 A3

A4 C3 C1 E1 A5 D4

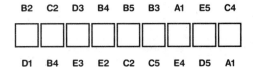

B2 C2 D3 B4 B5 B3 A1 E5 C4

D1 B4 E3 E2 C2 C5 E4 D5 A1

Answers see page 334

Puzzle 5

Look at the pattern of tiles. Which of the following tiles replaces the question mark?

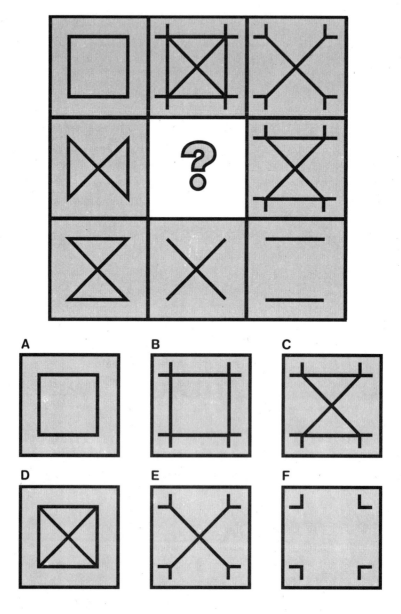

Answer see page 335

Puzzle 6

Which of the boxes should be used to replace the question mark?

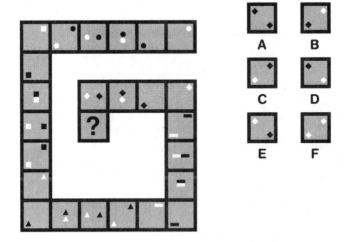

Puzzle 7

Which word is a synonym of EXPRESSIVE?

A. PARTICULAR

B. SUGGESTIVE

C. POSITIVE

D. MEANINGFUL

E. ELEGANT

Answers see page 335

Puzzle 8

Arrange the tiles in this diagram so that they form a square. When this is done correctly four words can be read down and across. What are the words?

Puzzle 9 – Sudoku

3		6	8					
	8					9	7	6
2								8
			9			3	8	
				1	4	2	9	
				8				5
	7	3	1	6		8		
	2			3				
	4	5			8			

Answers see page 336

Puzzle 10

Which of these boxes can be made from the template?

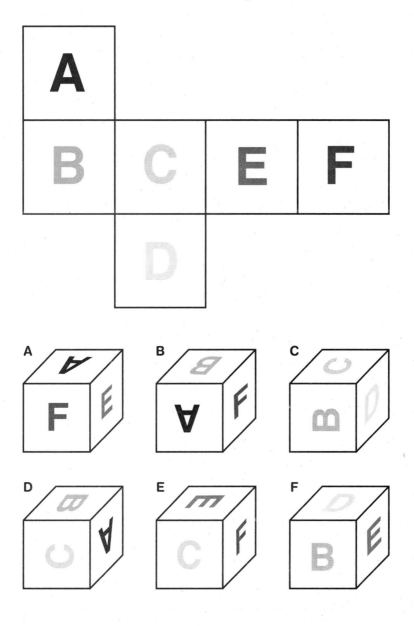

Answer see page 336

Puzzle 11

Complete the square with the letters of B R Y A N. When completed no row, column or diagonal line will contain the same letter more than once. One horizontal line will spell the name correctly.

What letter should replace the question mark?

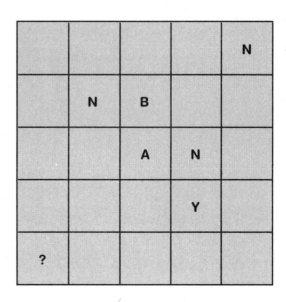

Puzzle 12 – Sudoku

	7						6	
2	6	1				3	7	9
		3				2		
			4		5			
3				8				5
7		9	3	1	2	6		4
			5		8			
5				2				3
8		4				5		7

Answers see page 336

Puzzle 13

Fill the numbers into the blank spaces. There is only one correct way.

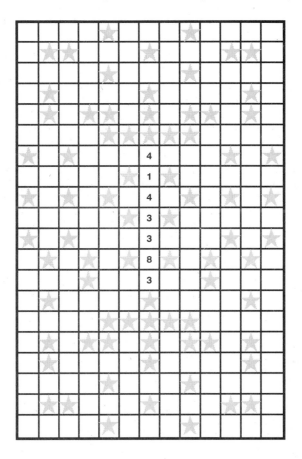

ACROSS

118	2133	6289
126	2345	6321
149	2801	9134
197	2803	9277
421	3458	9783
738	3482	12304
769	3485	12334
823	4190	12345
864	4227	53802
932	4656	56182
987	5199	0693878
1366	5660	9124914

DOWN

14	8228	443628
15	9998	492660
25	12735	536293
33	15787	593680
39	17151	4143383
42	24991	5428292
1178	26114	6132104
2119	64843	586713226
3002	116357	981921603
6334	200900	

Answer see page 337

Puzzle 14

How many ways are there to score 85 on this dartboard using four darts only?
Each dart always lands in a sector and no dart falls to the floor.

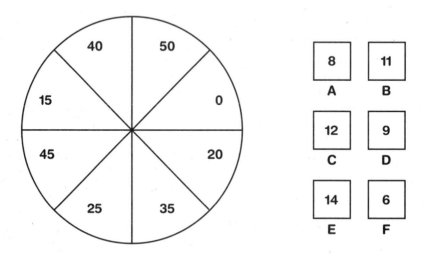

Puzzle 15

There is a somewhat confusing situation at the dog show this year. Four brothers – Andy, Bill, Colin and Donald – each enter two dogs, and each has named his dogs after two of his brothers. Consequently, there are two dogs named Andy, two named Bill, two named Colin and two named Donald.

Of the eight dogs, three are corgis, three labradors and two dalmatians. None of the four brothers owns two dogs of the same breed. No two dogs of the same breed have the same name. Neither of Andy's dogs is named Donald and neither of Colin's dogs is named Andy. No corgi is named Andy and no labrador is named Donald. Bill does not own a labrador.

Who are the owners of the dalmatians and what are the dalmatians' names?

Answers see page 338

Puzzle 16

In the grid below, the intersections have a value equal to the sum of their four touching numbers. Can you answer the questions at the bottom:

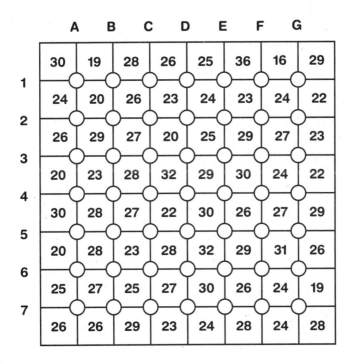

A. What are the grid references for the three intersection points with a value of 100?

B. Which intersection point/s has a value of 92?

C. How many intersections have a value of less than 100?

D. Which intersection has the highest value?

E. Which intersection has the lowest value?

F. Which intersection/s has a value of 115?

G. How many intersections have a value of 105 and which are they?

H. How many intersections have a value of 111 and which are they?

Answer see page 338

Puzzle 17 – Sudoku

	4	9	8		2			
	6				9			
		8				3		
		5					4	9
8								
	1	2	9					6
			2		8	7		1
			7				3	5
1				5				

Puzzle 18

If the names Diego Maradona and Jack Charlton are

⌐⌐⌐⌐⌐⌐ ⌐⌐⌐⌐⌐⌐⌐⌐

and

⌐⌐⌐⌐ ⌐⌐⌐⌐⌐⌐⌐⌐

Who are the other footballers?

1. ⌐⌐⌐⌐⌐⌐⌐ ⌐⌐⌐⌐⌐⌐
2. ⌐⌐⌐⌐⌐⌐⌐ ⌐⌐⌐⌐⌐⌐⌐⌐
3. ⌐⌐⌐⌐⌐ ⌐⌐⌐⌐⌐⌐
4. ⌐⌐⌐⌐⌐ ⌐⌐⌐⌐⌐⌐⌐⌐
5. ⌐⌐⌐⌐⌐⌐⌐ ⌐⌐⌐⌐⌐⌐⌐⌐⌐

Answers see page 338-9

Puzzle 19

Make a circle out of these shapes. When the correct circle has been found an English word can be read clockwise. What is the word?

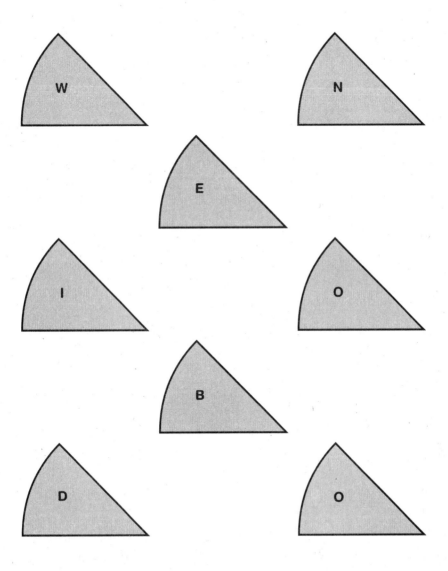

Answer see page 339

Puzzle 20

Look at the group of three squares. They have a certain feature which is shared by only one of the groups of three squares below. What is it, and which group matches?

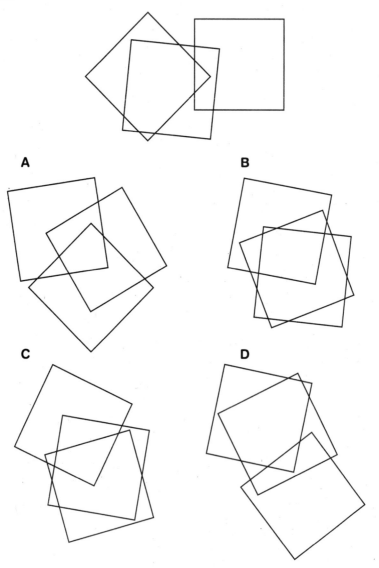

A

B

C

D

Answer see page 339

Puzzle 21

Here is a strange signpost to the burial grounds in Ancient Egypt. How far is it to burial ground of Thoth?

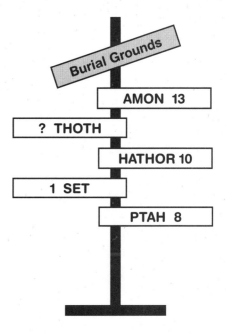

Puzzle 22 – Sudoku

		3						5
	1			6		9		
6			4	1	2			
4			2		9	6		
1	2	8				7		4
7			1		8	5		
5			8	2	1			
	7			5		2		
		2						1

Answers see page 339-40

Puzzle 23

What comes next in this series?

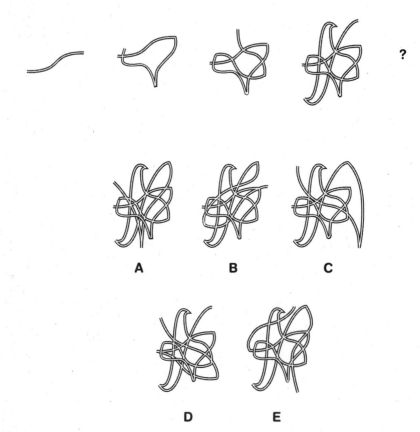

Answer see page 340

Puzzle 24

Draw three straight lines that make four sections with a total value of 40 in each, using the values given below. The lines do not have to go from one edge to another.

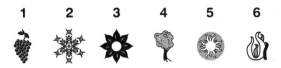

Answer see page 340

Puzzle 25

Which set of shapes fits into the middle of this panel to complete the pattern?

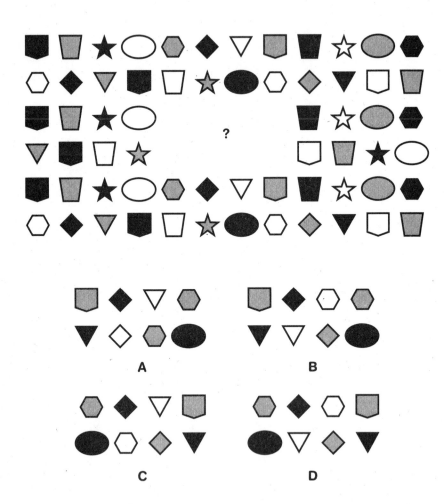

Answer see page 340

Puzzle 26

Find the 14 differences in picture B.

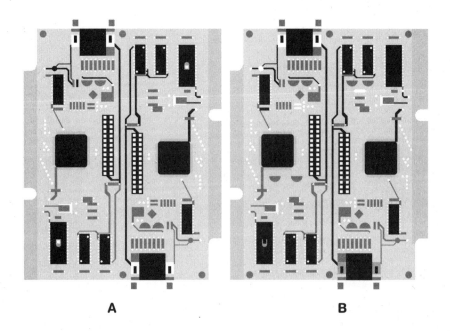

A   B

Answer see page 341

Puzzle 27

This is an unusual maze. Find four separate routes through it without any route crossing another, although the paths may merge. On each route collect 6 letters to give you four musical terms.

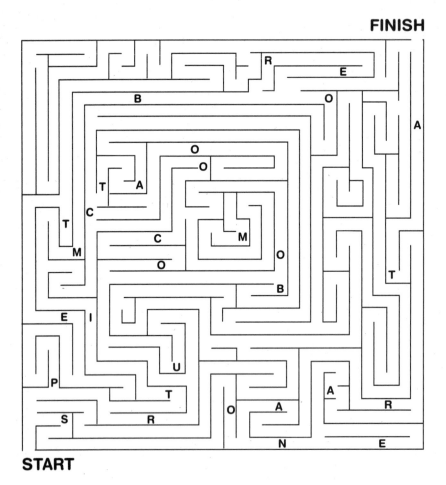

FINISH

START

Answer see page 341

Puzzle 28

Complete the two words using the letters of the following once only.

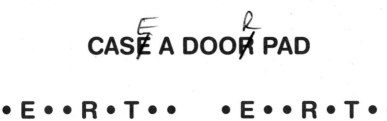

CAS*E* A DOO*R* PAD

• E • • R • T • •   • E • • R • T • •

Puzzle 29

Draw the next figure in this series.

Answers see page 341

Puzzle 30

Change the second letter of each word to the left and to the right. Two other English words must be formed. Place the letter used in the empty section. When this has been completed, for all the words, another English word can be read down.

What is the word?

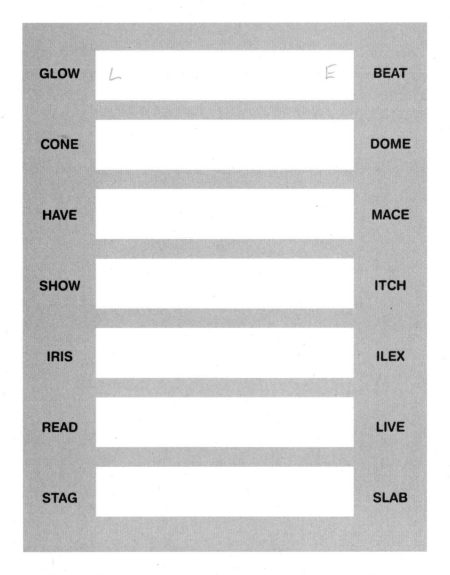

GLOW	L	E	BEAT
CONE			DOME
HAVE			MACE
SHOW			ITCH
IRIS			ILEX
READ			LIVE
STAG			SLAB

Answer see page 342

Puzzle 31

Put a value from below into each triangle so that the total in each square gives a value that makes each row, column, and long diagonal add to 203.

6 8 29 9 27 30 13 7 3 29 14 15 8

3 2 19 11 12 39 0 40 1 7 11 2 9 2

34 13 10 8 12 20 19 36 5 4 5 18 40

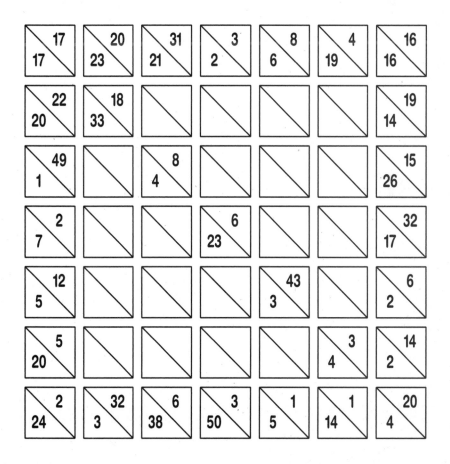

Answer see page 342

Puzzle 32 – Sudoku

				1		4		
5			6	2	3			
	1			5			6	7
3			8					4
					5		7	9
1			2					6
9	3	5				6	4	2
2			5		6	7	9	
				9	2	5		

Puzzle 33

Place the letters shown into the diagram in such a way that three words can be read across and one down the middle. What are the words?

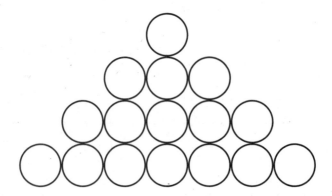

A   B   D   E   E   E   J   K   L   L   M   N   O   T   W   W

Answers see page 342

Puzzle 34

Can you find the following tools and equipment in the puzzle below?

HAMMER	CHISEL	DRILL
PUNCH	SCREWDRIVER	RIVETS
BRADAWL	SAW	MACHINERY
TOOLBELT	NAILS	KNIVES
PLIERS	SPANNER	RATCHET
HANDPLANE	PINCERS	SAFETY HELMET
FILE	COUNTERSINKER	TILES

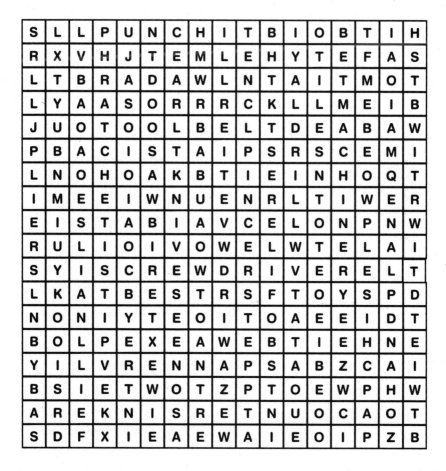

Answer see page 343

Puzzle 35

Discover the connection between the letters and the numbers. Which number should replace the question mark?

A	1	B
D	7	K
Q	2	O
R	2	T
Z	?	C

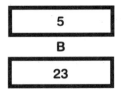

12

A

5

B

20

C

28

D

23

E

9

F

Puzzle 36

The wordframe below, when filled with the correct letters, will give the name of a US city. There are two possible letters for each square, one right and one wrong.

What is the city?

	A	B	C	D	E
1	I	D	B	F	T
2	Y	N	Q	G	C
3	V	J	H	R	X
4	M	A	E	K	P
5	C	Z	S	O	U

2E	3C	1A	4B	4B	2D	3A
1B	4D	2B	2E	2D	1E	5D

Answers see page 343

Puzzle 1

If the following says :

THREE WHEELER FOLLOWS VEGAN,

What do the characters below say?

The letters have been mixed up but all letters of the same colour belong together.

Puzzle 2

Start at any corner and follow the lines. Collect another four boxes. Green boxes are worth 2 each, red boxes are worth 4 and blue boxes are worth 3. Total the five boxes. What is the highest possible total?

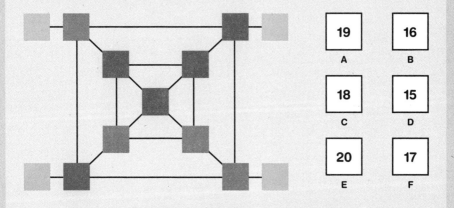

19	**16**
A	B
18	**15**
C	D
20	**17**
E	F

Answers see page 160

Puzzle 3

Which of the sections shown would logically complete the puzzle?

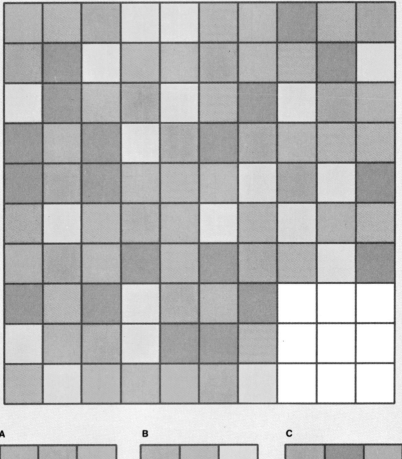

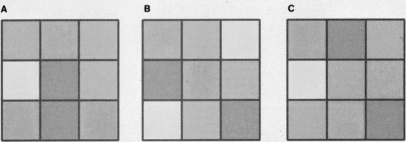

Answer see page 160

Puzzle 4

Three countries can be found in the diagram. The letters are written in the correct order. Only three different shades of colour are used in each name. What are the countries?

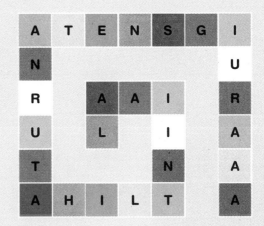

Puzzle 5

The numbers contain a hidden message. What is it?

7	12	19	2	18	14	5
8	9	18	26	4	18	21
15	17	12	15	9	25	22
19	7	26	24	19	8	14
9	23	13	19	6	7	12
23	5	22	3	21	15	24
12	23	10	14	11	15	22

Answers see page 160

Puzzle 6

Which of these is the odd one out?

A

B

C

D

E

Answer see page 160

Puzzle 7

Which square's contents matches B1?

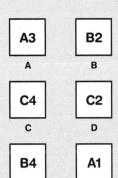

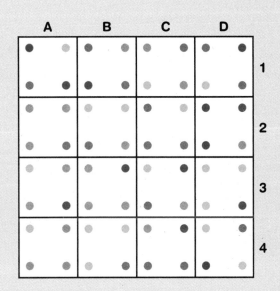

Puzzle 8

Find a number that could replace the question mark. Each colour represents a number under 10.

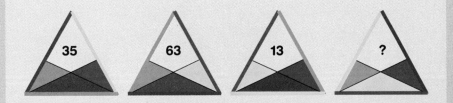

Answers see page 160

Puzzle 9

The direction in which the arrows point is in some way related to their colour. Would an orange arrow point up or down?

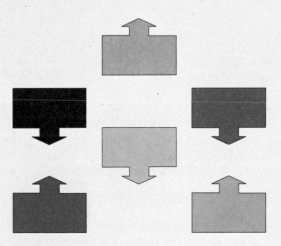

Puzzle 10

Each same box has a value. Work out the logic and discover what should replace the question mark.

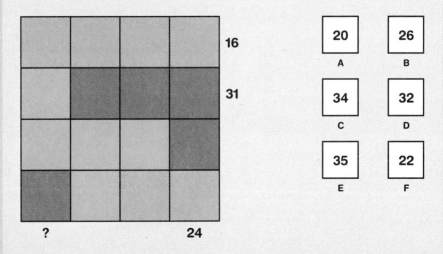

Answers see page 160

Puzzle 11

Which of the constructed boxes can be made from the pattern?

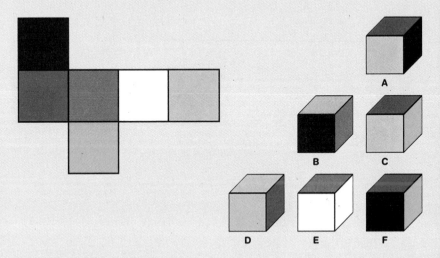

Puzzle 12

What number should replace the question mark? Each colour represents a value under 10.

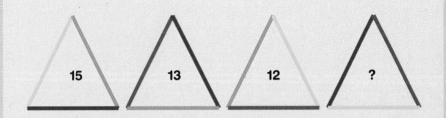

15   13   12   ?

Answers see page 160

Puzzle 13

The two pictures are identical except for ten alterations made to the second version. See if you can spot the ten differences.

Answer see page 160

Puzzle 14

A dark blue circle is worth 3, a yellow circle 4, a pink one 6, a light blue one 5 and a red one 8. Black is minus 3. Follow the arrows from the bottom left to the top right. Total the circles as you go. What is the lowest total possible?

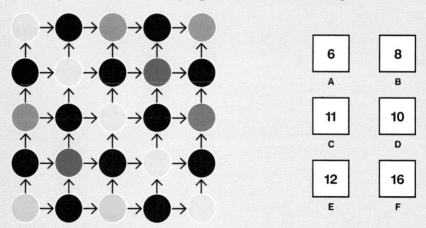

6	**8**
A	B
11	**10**
C	D
12	**16**
E	F

Puzzle 15

Find a number that could replace the question mark. Each colour represents a number under 10.

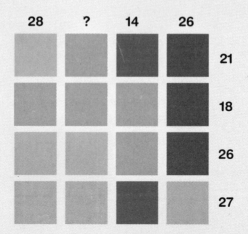

Answers see page 160

Puzzle 16

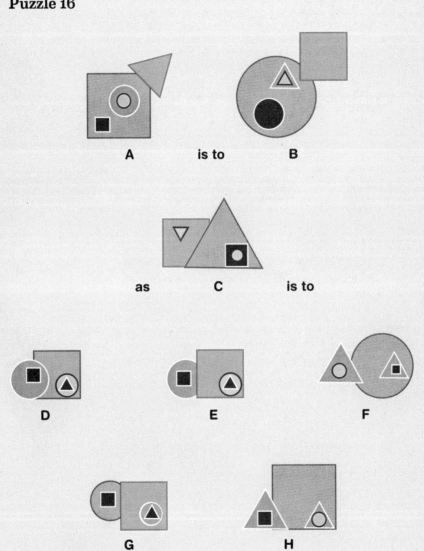

A   is to   B

as   C   is to

D   E   F

G   H

Answer see page 160

Puzzle 17

Find a number that could replace the question mark. Each colour represents a number under 10.

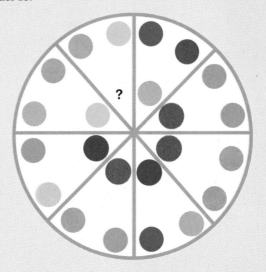

Puzzle 18

The colours all have a numerical value, and one of the shapes also has a mathematical significance. When you have worked out what the colours and shapes mean you will be able to find the missing number.

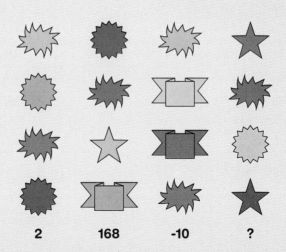

2   **168**   **-10**   **?**

Answers see page 160

Puzzle 19

Fill the diagram up with circles. The black circle goes in the middle and represents the letter M. Red circles are Is, blue circles are Ns, and green circles are Ds. When the correct pattern has been found, by moving from circle to touching circle, including in diagonal leaps, and in each case starting at the black circle, the letters of the word MIND can be traced 17 times. What does the pattern look like?

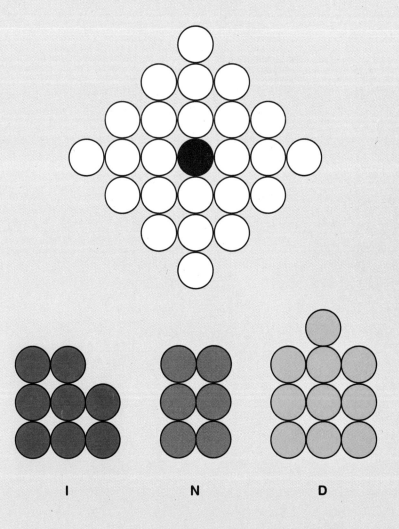

I   N   D

Answer see page 160

Puzzle 20

Find a number that could replace the question mark. Each colour represents a number under 10.

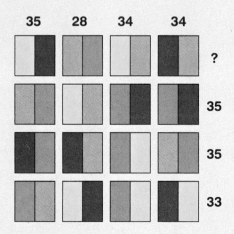

35	28	34	34	
				?
				35
				35
				33

Puzzle 21

Which well known expression is represented by this rebus?

Answers see page 160

Puzzle 22

Can you crack the colour code and make your way from one blue square to the other? Each colour takes you up, down, left or right. The blue arrow tells you which way is up.

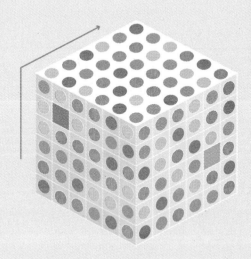

Puzzle 23

What percentage of this grid is green and what percentage is pink?

Answers see page 160

Solutions

1. Where have all the flowers gone.

2. C.

3. C. Each row and column must contain two orange and two green squares.

4. Argentina, Australia and Lithuania.

5. Take only the red numbers. They represent letters of the alphabet numbered backwards (Z = 1, A = 26). The message is: 'This will be hard to decode'.

6. C. In all other cases the first letters of the colours form words: gory, poor, prop, orgy.

7. C.

8. 27. The colours are worth: yellow 2, red 3, green 4, purple 6. Multiply the sides of the triangle together to get Result 1. Add the inner numbers together to get Result 2. Now subtract R2 from R1 to get the answer.

9. Up. Arrows with colours with an E in their name point upwards.

10. B. Pink=4, blue=8, green=7.

11. C.

12. 14. The colors are worth: red 5, yellow 3, green 6, blue 4. Add the sides together and swap the results within horizontally adjacent triangles.

13.

14. D.

15. 27. Colours are worth: orange 8, green 4, red 3, purple 6.

16. E. A square becomes a circle, a circle a triangle, and a triangle a square of similar proportions and positions.

17. 6. The colors are worth: red 1, orange 2, green 3, yellow 4, pink 5, purple 6, brown 7. Add the outer numbers and put the sum in the center of the opposite segment.

18. 127. The colours have their alphanumeric values but the alphabet has been numbered backwards (Z = 1, A = 26). All the shapes are added except for the explosion which is always subtracted.

19.

20. 28. Colors are worth: purple 5, orange 2, yellow 3, green 6. Add colours in each square together.

21. In the pink.

22.

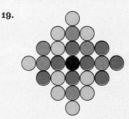

23. 52% is pink, 48% is green. 13 out of 25 squares in the grid are pink, 12 are green. Multiply both numbers by 4 and you see a percentage.

Puzzle 37

The numbers 4–16 have already been inserted into the grid, almost – but not quite – at random. Following just two simple rules, where would you place the numbers 1, 2 and 3 in the grid?

	14	10	7
9	6		4
16		13	11
12	8	5	15

Puzzle 38

DOUBT : CONVICTION

Which two words below have the same relationship as the two words above?

A. faultless : exemplary

B. fastidious : slender

C. courage : resolution

D. instinct : constancy

E. routine : abnormal

Answers see page 343-4

Puzzle 39

The graph below shows the examination results of students taking their school leaving exams. 30 children took tests.

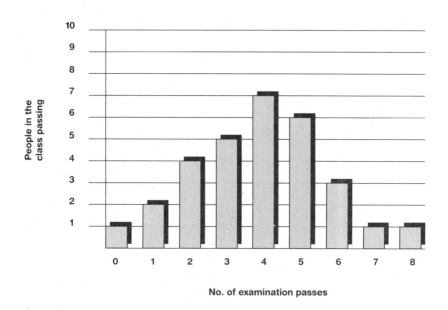

No. of examination passes

A. What was the average number of exam passes per student?

B. If the top 5 students were not in this class, what would have been the average number of exam passes per student?

C. If 10% took 8 tests, 70% took 6 tests and 20% took 4 tests, how many test papers had a fail mark?

Answer see page 344

Puzzle 40 – Sudoku

6					5			
		4			7		5	3
	7					2		1
			7		9			
	1			2			4	
			1		3			
8		5					6	
1	3		8			7		
			9					5

Puzzle 41

Which day is two days before the day after the day three days after the day before Tuesday?

SUNDAY

MONDAY

TUESDAY

WEDNESDAY

THURSDAY

FRIDAY

SATURDAY

Answers see page 344

Puzzle 42

Three college students – Anne, Bess and Candice – each study four subjects. Two of them study physics; two study algebra; two study English; two study history; two study French; two study Japanese.

Anne: if she studies algebra then she also takes history & French;
          if she studies history she does not take English or physics;
          if she studies English she does not take Japanese or algebra.
Bess: if she studies English she also takes Japanese and physics;
          if she studies Japanese she does not take algebra or French;
          if she studies algebra she does not take English or Japanese.
Candice: if she studies French she also takes algebra and English;
          if she does not study algebra she studies Japanese and History;
          if she studies Japanese she does not take English or physics.

What do you know about these three students?

	Anne	Bess	Candice
Physics			
Algebra			
English			
History			
French			
Japanese			

Answer see page 345

Puzzle 43

Use three straight lines to divide this square into five sections, each of which contains a total value of 60.

```
1   9   3   7       1       4   9   3
        0       3
  7   9   8   3       3   5 9
    7       0       0
8       1   1       0     7
    5     1
  0             6   2
2   0   5       0 6       0
 8           7 7       2     9
    9       8 3
          3     4       7   0
    3       9
        1         1 7
 2   0   4     3 6
  8   1     2       5   3
    7         0
1   5           4   2   5 3
  5   4     4     2 9
```

Puzzle 44

This is a Meaningless signpost. but there is a twisted form of logic behind the figures. Discover the logic and find the distance to Chicago. How far is it?

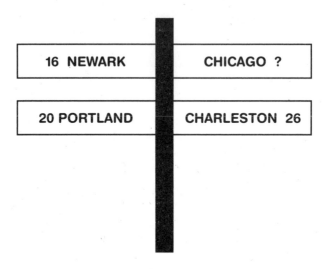

Puzzle 45 – Sudoku

							8	
6		5		1	8	4	7	
4		2						
3				2				
			1	4	6			
				5				9
						2		3
	2	4	6	3		7		5
	5							

Answers see page 345

Puzzle 46

Which of the constructed boxes cannot be made from the pattern?

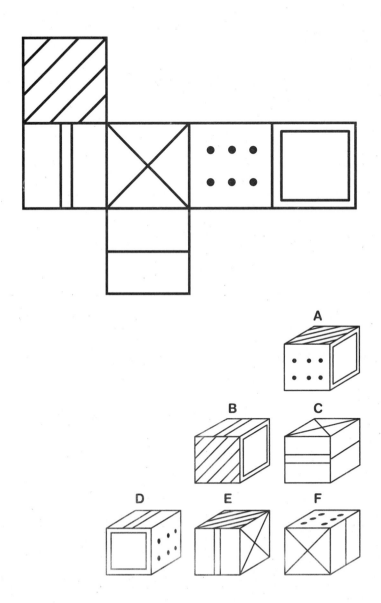

Answer see page 346

Puzzle 47

Look at the above sequence. Which of options 1–6 becomes J and which N?

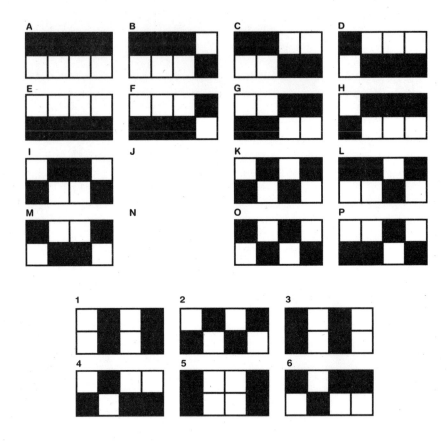

Answer see page 346

Puzzle Mix 4

Puzzle 1

There are five pupils, each in a different class. Each pupil takes a subject and sport which she enjoys.

1. The girl who plays squash likes algebra and is not in class 5.
2. Doris is in class 3 and Betty likes running.
3. The girl who likes running is in class 2.
4. The girl in class 4 likes swimming, while Elizabeth likes chemistry.
5. Alice is in class 6 and likes squash but not geography.
6. The girl who likes chemistry also enjoys basketball.
7. The girl who likes biology also likes running.
8. Clara likes history but not tennis.

Work out the class, subject and sport of each girl.

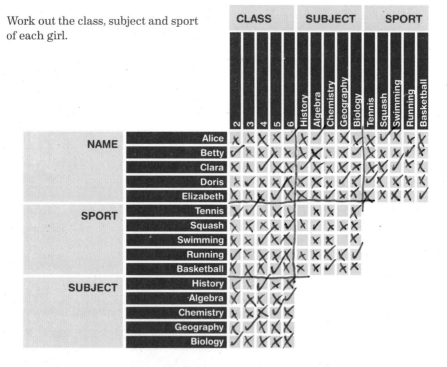

Name	Class	Subject	Sport
Alice	6	Algebra	Squash
Betty	2	Biology	Running
Clara	4	History	Swimming
Doris	3	Geography	Tennis
Elizabeth	5	Chemistry	Basketball

Answer see page 347

Puzzle 2 – Sudoku

7			9		2			5
8			4		6			9
3				5				4
		5				4		
9				8				7
	9		2		8		4	
		6		1		8		
	3						7	

Puzzle 3

What letter has been missed from the last box?

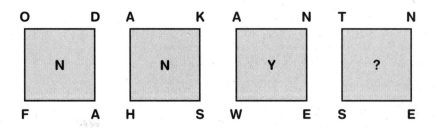

Puzzle 4

The names of the following ten film stars can be found in this grid on vertical, horizontal and diagonal lines. Can you find them?

John Cleese

Tom Cruise

Mel Gibson

Hugh Grant

Tom Hanks

Val Kilmer

Bruce Lee

Al Pacino

Sean Penn

Brad Pitt

W	Z	Q	E	P	R	V	H	E	F	M
T	O	U	S	Y	J	A	H	E	E	Z
T	N	S	I	G	K	L	U	L	S	W
I	I	E	U	F	H	K	G	E	E	P
P	C	A	R	H	X	I	H	C	E	H
D	A	N	C	H	B	L	G	U	L	J
A	P	P	M	S	Q	M	R	R	C	R
R	L	E	O	J	R	E	A	B	N	G
B	A	N	T	T	Z	R	N	P	H	Y
S	K	N	A	H	M	O	T	W	O	S
Y	R	B	X	F	Q	J	X	N	J	S

Answer see page 348

Puzzle 5

Which of the following is not an anagram of a fruit?

A. MINK PUP

B. BURY REBEL

C. USA MAST

D. MANS GUT

E. DAMN RAIN

Puzzle 6

Take one letter from each bottle in order to find 5 insects.

Answers see page 348

Puzzle 7

A woman usually leaves work at 5.30pm, calls at the supermarket, then catches the 6pm train, which arrives at the station in her home town at 6.30pm. Her husband leaves home each day, drives to the station and picks her up at 6.30pm, just as she gets off the train.

Today the woman finishes work about five minutes earlier than usual, decides to go straight to the station instead of calling at the supermarket, and manages to catch the 5.30pm train, which arrives at her home station at 6pm. Since her husband is not there to pick her up she begins to walk home. Her husband leaves home at the usual time, sees his wife walking, turns around, picks her up and drives home, arriving there 10 minutes earlier than usual.

Assume that all the trains arrive precisely on time. For how long does the woman walk before her husband picks her up?

Answer see page 348

Puzzle 8

Fill the numbers into the blank spaces. There is only one correct way.

ACROSS

30	306	619	2768259
74	326	649	4346540
87	359	659	5783968
93	386	691	6281307
018	390	697	6445535
042	467	721	6490916
133	496	735	6906308
148	516	929	7590936
273	519	954	9473460
298	563	989	9798259

DOWN

043	928	2369674	7533652
192	165263	3268959	7934895
313	320469	4906736	9219367
333	372108	5176453	9452695
344	697469	5364749	9497059
460	0840396	6089148	9687097
521	0929969	7485571	9759968
863			

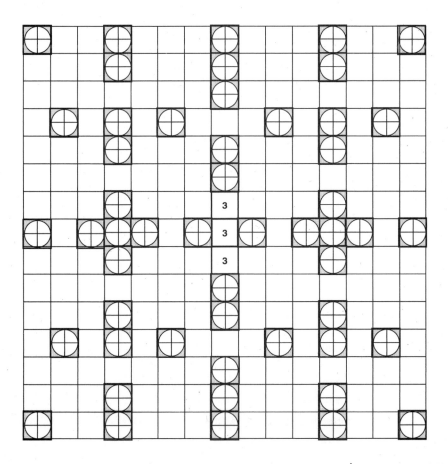

Answer see page 349

Puzzle 9

Take the letters and arrange them correctly in the column under which they appear. Once this has been done the name of a famous person will emerge.

What is the name?

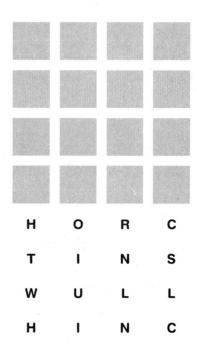

H	O	R	C
T	I	N	S
W	U	L	L
H	I	N	C

Puzzle 10 – Sudoku

		7	2					
	3							7
1					7	9	4	
5						7	8	
		8			4		5	
4						1	2	
9					6	2	1	
	1							5
		3	1					

Answers see page 350

Puzzle 11

Six children have invented a card game and scoring system. It uses the cards up to 10, at face value, with aces scoring 1. In each round, the value of the card dealt is added to that child's score. Diamonds are worth double the face value. If two or more children are dealt cards with the same face value in one round, they lose the value of that card instead of gaining it (diamonds still doubled). They are each dealt six cards face up as shown below:

Player	Round 1	Round 2	Round 3	Round 4	Round 5	Round 6
1	6 ♥	3 ♠	ACE ♦	9 ♣	10 ♥	4 ♠
2	10 ♠	ACE ♠	7 ♥	6 ♦	5 ♠	8 ♣
3	7 ♦	8 ♥	4 ♣	3 ♥	ACE ♣	5 ♣
4	4 ♥	9 ♦	7 ♠	5 ♦	10 ♣	3 ♦
5	8 ♠	5 ♥	6 ♠	9 ♠	2 ♠	4 ♦
6	3 ♣	2 ♣	9 ♥	7 ♣	10 ♦	8 ♦

When the scores are added up, which player:

1. Came third?

2. Won?

3. Came last?

4. Was winning after the fourth cards had been dealt?

5. Had even scores?

6. Had a score divisible by 3?

7. What was the second highest score?

8 What was the sum of all of the scores?

Answer see page 350

Puzzle 12 – Sudoku

		6						
		2					9	5
3				8	2	4		7
8	7		4					
				9				
					6		1	3
2		8	6	5				4
4	1					9		
						2		

Puzzle 13

Out of this list of stock the number of packets of food are written. The numbers bear a relationship to the letters in the words. What should replace the question mark?

PIZZA

BURGER

STEAK

FRIES

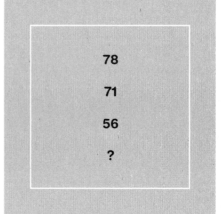

78

71

56

?

Answers see page 350-1

Puzzle 14

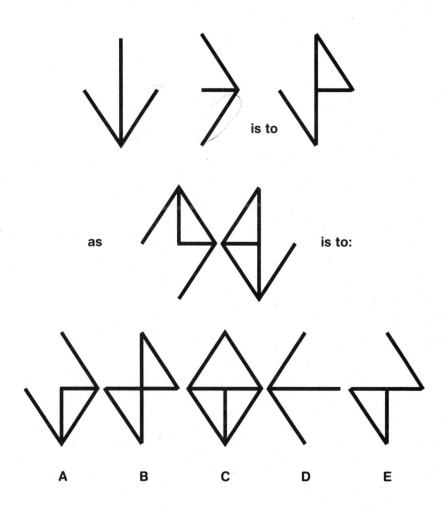

Puzzle 15

Place one letter in the middle of this diagram. Four five-letter words can now be arranged from each straight line of letters. What is the letter and what are the words?

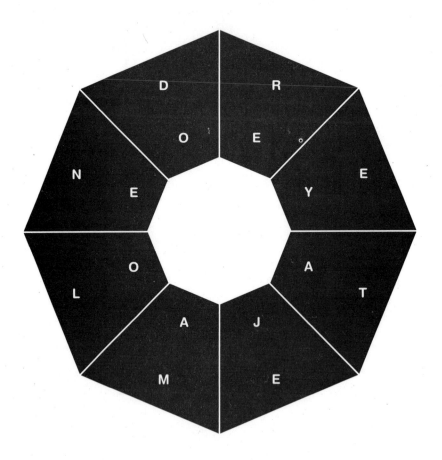

Answer see page 351

Puzzle 16

Which of the slices should be used to complete the cake so that the top half matches the bottom half?

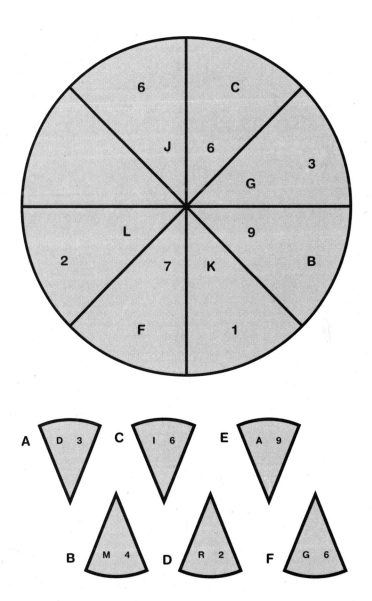

Answer see page 351

Puzzle 17

Four husband and wife couples go to see a play. They all sit in the same row, but no husband sits next to his wife, and a man and a woman are at opposite ends of the row. Their names are Andrews, Barker, Collins and Dunlop.

1. Mrs Dunlop or Mr Andrews is in the end seat.
2. Mr Andrews is mid-way between Mr Collins and Mrs Collins.
3. Mr Collins is two seats from Mrs Dunlop.
4. Mrs Collins is mid-way between Mr and Mrs Barker.
5. Mrs Andrews is next to the end seat.
6. Mr Dunlop is two seats from Mr Andrews.
7. Mrs Collins is closer to the right end than the left end.

Work out the seating arrangements along the row.

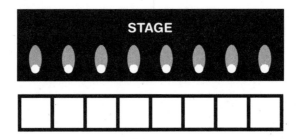

Answer see page 352

Puzzle 18

A knight, which moves either one square horizontally and two vertically or two horizontally and one vertically, starts at the shaded square of this chess board visiting each square without returning to the same square twice. Find the route which spells out six famous movie stars.

O	T	E	S	I	O	T	I
M	O	P	S	L	B	G	R
E	O	G	N	D	N	G	O
N	E	B	O	R	A	I	O
H	V	E	J	D	L	M	T
S	R	A	E	F	D	R	N
E	W	B	U	A	I	R	C
O	I	M	N	E	R	E	T

Answer see page 352

Puzzle 19 – Sudoku

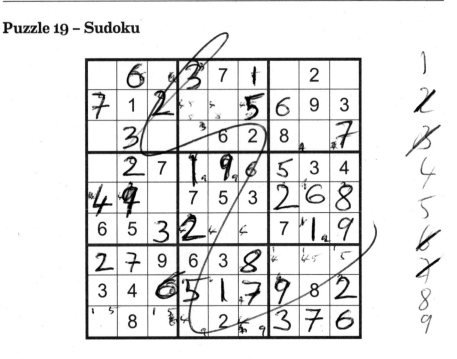

Puzzle 20

Insert the correct mathematical signs between each number in order to resolve the equation. What are the signs?

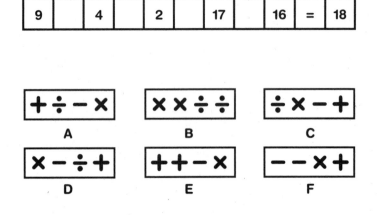

Answers see page 352

Puzzle 21

At the carnival five boys of different ages eat different foods and take different rides.

1. Ron eats ice cream, Joe does not chew gum.
2. Sam, who is 14 years old, is not on the mountain.
3. The boy on the crocodile is 15 years old.
4. Len is not on the dodgems; Don is on the whirligig.
5. The boy eating ice cream is 13 years old.
6. The boy on the dodgems is eating a hot dog.
7. Joe eats fries on the big dipper.
8. Don, who is 12, is eating candy floss.

Work out the details of each boy.

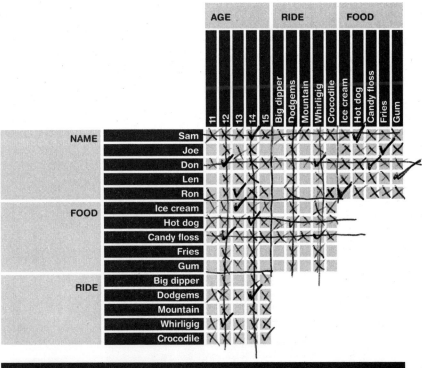

Name	Age	Ride	Food
SAM	14	DODGEMS	HOT DOG
JOE	11	15 CROC	FRIES
DON	12	WHIRLIGIG	CANDY FLOSS
LEN	11	15 CROC	GUM
RON	13	BIG DIP / MOUNTAIN	ICE-CREAM

15 = CROC

Answer see page 353

Puzzle 22

Five men and five women went to five different cities by five different modes of transport. From the information below, sort out which pair went together to which city and by which mode of transport.

1. The ferry was used to get to Paris, Alf went with Katie.
2. Bob went by bus, Sally went to Rome.
3. Len went by plane, the cruise went to New York.
4. Mary went to Madrid, Sam went with Judith.
5. Ben went by train, Fiona went to Berlin.
6. Alf went to New York, Judith went by ferry.
7. Kate went on a cruise, Len went to Rome.
8. Mary went by bus, Ben went to Berlin.

		Sally	Judith	Kate	Mary	Fiona	Cruise	Ferry	Bus	Plane	Train	Paris	Berlin	Madrid	Rome	New York
MAN	Bob															
	Sam															
	Alf															
	Len															
	Ben															
CITY	Paris															
	Berlin															
	Madrid															
	Rome															
	New York															
TRANSPORT	Cruise															
	Ferry															
	Bus															
	Plane															
	Train															

Male	Female	City	Transport

Answer see page 353

Puzzle 23

Five men went to a fancy dress ball. Each went as a different character, had a different costume, and danced a different dance

1. Simon wore a fedora, Henrry danced the Bossa-Nova.
2. Dr Jekyll Jitterbugged, Robert went as Napoleon.
3. Morris went as Shakespeare, Peter wore a homburg.
4. Frankenstein danced the Palais Glide.
5. Peter danced the Palais Glide.
6. The man in the jackboots danced the Charleston
7. The man who danced the Barn Dance wore a skull-cap.
8. Dracula wore leggings, Robert wore jackboots.

Can you match the men to their character, costume and dance?

	FANCY DRESS					CLOTHES					DANCE				
	Dracula	Napoleon	Dr Jekyll	Frankenstein	Shakespeare	Leggings	Jack Boots	Fedora	Homburg	Skull-cap	Bossa-Nova	Charleston	Jitterbug	Palais Glide	Barn Dance
NAME Simon															
Morris															
Henry															
Peter															
Robert															
DANCE Barn Dance															
Charleston															
Palais Glide															
Bossa Nova															
Jitter Bug															
CLOTHES Homburg															
Skull-cap															
Fedora															
Jack Boots															
Leggings															

Name	Fancy Dress	Clothes	Dance

Answer see page 353

Puzzle 24

A group of friends get together with their daughters for the evening.

1. John is 52 years old and his daughter is not called Eve.
2. Len has a daughter aged 21 years, and Betty is three years older than Eve.
3. Kevin is 53 years old and Diana is 19 years old.
4. Eve is 18 years old, and Nick has a daughter called Carol.
5. Alison is 20 years old and her father is called John.
6. Kevin has a daughter aged 19 years, and Eve's father is called Malcolm.
7. Malcolm is three years older than Nick.

Father	Daughter	Father's age	Daughter's age

Answers see page 353

Puzzle 25

A woman has a garden path 2m wide, demarcated with pebbles, which spiral tightly into the middle of the garden. One day the woman walks the length of the path, finishing in the middle. Ignore the width of the hedge and assume she walks in the middle of the path. How far does she walk?

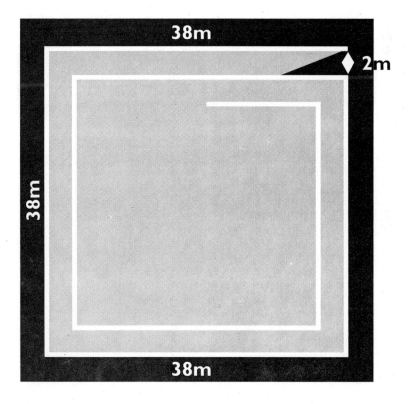

Answers see page 354

Puzzle 26

What is the smallest number of segments of equal area and shape that the rectangle can be divided into so that each segment contains the same number of triangles?

Answer see page 354

Puzzle 27

What word can be placed in front of the other five to form five new words? Each dot represents a letter.

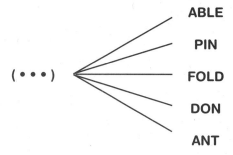

(• • •)

ABLE

PIN

FOLD

DON

ANT

Puzzle 28

Fill in the missing letters to find food on the menu.

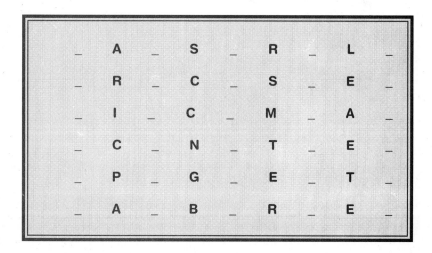

_ A _ S _ R _ L _

_ R _ C _ S _ E _

_ I _ C _ M _ A _

_ C _ N _ T _ E _

_ P _ G _ E _ T _

_ A _ B _ R _ E _

Answers see page 354

Puzzle 29 – Sudoku

4		6				1	8	3
5			8					
	9							
			4	3		6	2	
				1				
	7	3		2	8			
							9	
					5			8
8	1	7				5		4

Puzzle 30

What is the missing value of this logic series?

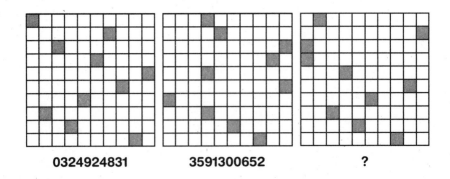

0324924831   **3591300652**   **?**

Answers see page 355

Puzzle 31

If the word scientist is ⌐∴|∙∙ ⌐⌐∙|∙|∙∙ ⌐⌐

who are these scientists?

1. ⌐|∙∙ ⌐∙ ⌐ ⌐⌐|∙|∙∙ ⌐

2. ∙⌐|⌐∷⌐|∙∙ ⌐⌐

3. ⌐|⌐|⌐ ⌐⌐|⌐

4. ∙⌐|⌐⌐|⌐∷⌐|∙∙ ∙⌐⌐⌐

5. ⌐⌐⌐∙∙|⌐∷

6. |⌐|⌐∷⌐|∙∙ ⌐

Puzzle 32 – Sudoku

							4	3
	3				7			2
9				1		8		
		1			9		2	
		8	3			6		
	7			5				
8				6	4			
			2				1	
3		5				4		

Answers see page 355

Puzzle 33

In this grid the word 'TIPTOE', written without a change of direction appears only once. It can be written forwards or backwards in a horizontal, vertical or diagonal direction. Can you spot it?

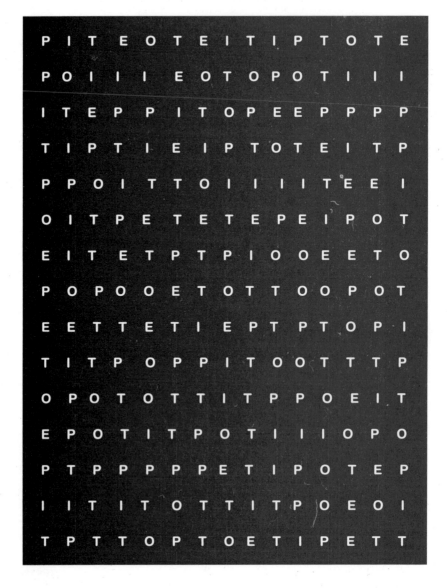

Answer see page 356

Puzzle 34

When the tiles in this square are rearranged a logical pattern will emerge. Which of the tiles should be used to complete the square?

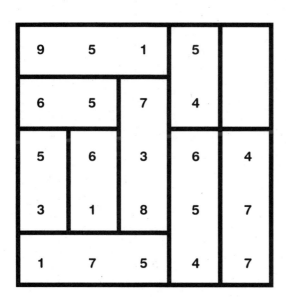

Puzzle 35

Can you work out what letter needs to be inserted in the middle to form four artists by combining opposite segments?

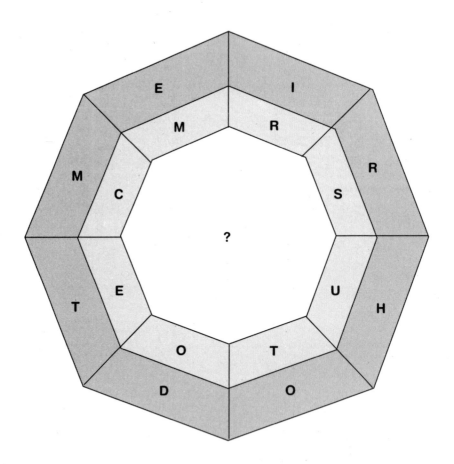

Answer see page 356

Puzzle 36

These clocks follow a weird kind of logic. What time should the fourth clock show? Choose from the four options provided.

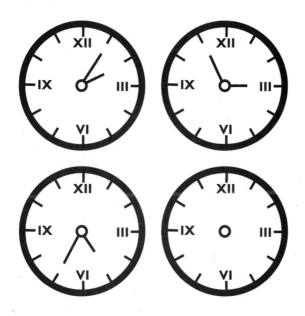

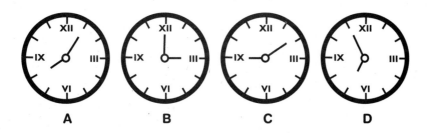

Answers see page 356

Puzzle 37

Discover the connection between the letters and the numbers. Which number should replace the question mark?

F	136	M
U	421	D
H	178	Q
O	115	A
X	?	I

672	834	411
A	B	C

295	118	924
D	E	F

Puzzle 38

Place two three-letter segments together to form a shade.

ISE SCA YEL LEW CER LET

Answers see page 357

Puzzle 39

The names of the following ten tennis players can be found in this grid on vertical, horizontal and diagonal lines. Can you find them?

Jeremy Bates
Pat Cash
Wayne Ferreira
Ivan Lendl
Jana Novotna

Marc Rosset
Greg Rusedski
Monica Seles
Michael Stich
Helena Sukova

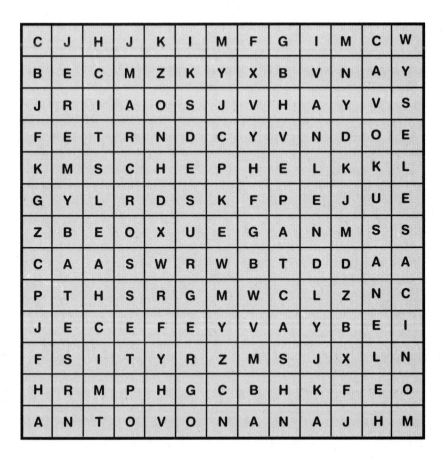

C	J	H	J	K	I	M	F	G	I	M	C	W
B	E	C	M	Z	K	Y	X	B	V	N	A	Y
J	R	I	A	O	S	J	V	H	A	Y	V	S
F	E	T	R	N	D	C	Y	V	N	D	O	E
K	M	S	C	H	E	P	H	E	L	K	K	L
G	Y	L	R	D	S	K	F	P	E	J	U	E
Z	B	E	O	X	U	E	G	A	N	M	S	S
C	A	A	S	W	R	W	B	T	D	D	A	A
P	T	H	S	R	G	M	W	C	L	Z	N	C
J	E	C	E	F	E	Y	V	A	Y	B	E	I
F	S	I	T	Y	R	Z	M	S	J	X	L	N
H	R	M	P	H	G	C	B	H	K	F	E	O
A	N	T	O	V	O	N	A	N	A	J	H	M

Answer see page 357

Puzzle 40

Make a circle out of these shapes. When the correct circle has been found an English word can be read clockwise. What is the word?

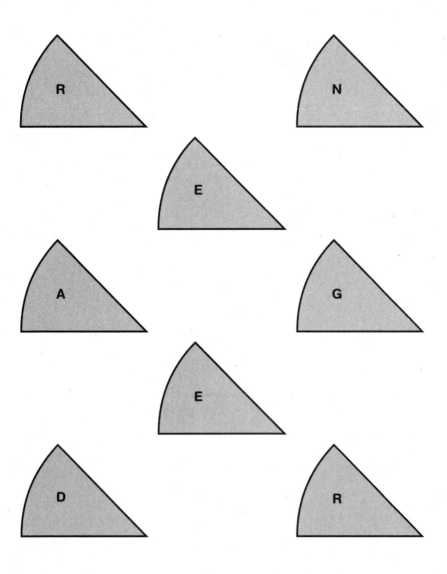

Answer see page 357

Puzzle 41 – Sudoku

			3			8		5
	9			7				
	3				6		7	
1			2					
		6		3		1	4	
8			9					
	2				9		5	
	8			4				
			7			9		8

Puzzle 42

Arrange the tiles in this diagram so that they form a square. When this is done correctly five words can be read down and across. What are the words?

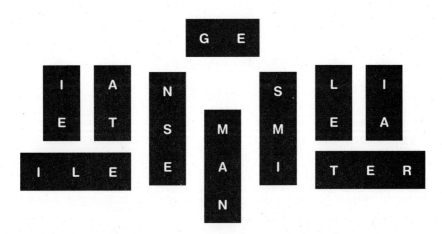

Answers see page 358

Puzzle 43

Insert the supplied rows of numbers into the appropriate places in the grid to make all rows, columns and long diagonals add to 175.

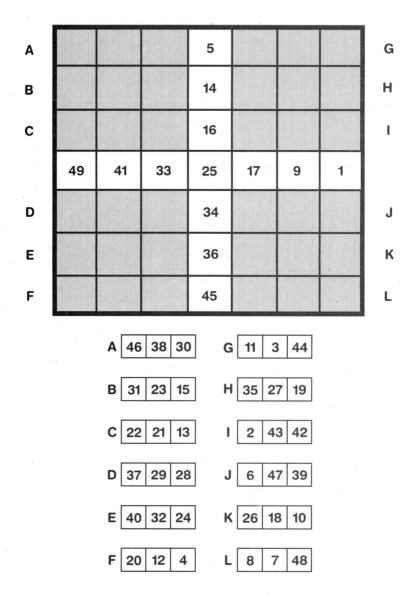

A	46	38	30		G	11	3	44
B	31	23	15		H	35	27	19
C	22	21	13		I	2	43	42
D	37	29	28		J	6	47	39
E	40	32	24		K	26	18	10
F	20	12	4		L	8	7	48

Answer see page 358

Puzzle 44

Which English word of three letters can be attached to the front of the words shown in the diagram to create six other words?

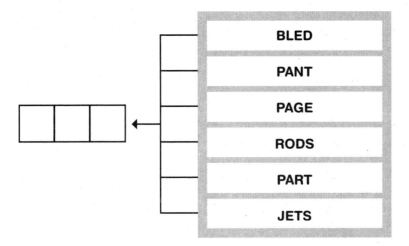

Puzzle 45

Mr Smith went on vacation to America

He liked New York

But not Maine

He liked Colorado

But not Wisconsin

He liked Nevada

But not Chicago

He liked Dallas

But not Michigan

Did he like Idaho?

Answers see page 358-9

Puzzle Mix 4

Puzzle 46 – Sudoku

					8	5	1	
	6							
				5		8	4	
			2	6	3			1
		7	5					
3			1			2		4
8		5			4			
9		3						
			9		5			2

Answers see page 359

Puzzle Mix 5

Puzzle 1 – Sudoku

3	9			5		4		
6			7					
						2		1
	7				1			2
5				8			1	
			3		6			5
1		9						
				6				9
		4	9		8		7	

Puzzle 2

GIBE is to TAUNT as BADINAGE is to:

A. PRANK

B. REPARTEE

C. PLEASANTRY

D. WITTICISM

E. JOKE

Answers see page 360

Puzzle 3

Each of the nine squares in the grid marked 1A to 3C should incorporate all of the items which are shown in the squares of the same letter and number, at the left and top, respectively. For example, 2B should incorporate all of the symbols that are in squares 2 and B. One square, however, is incorrect. Which one is it?

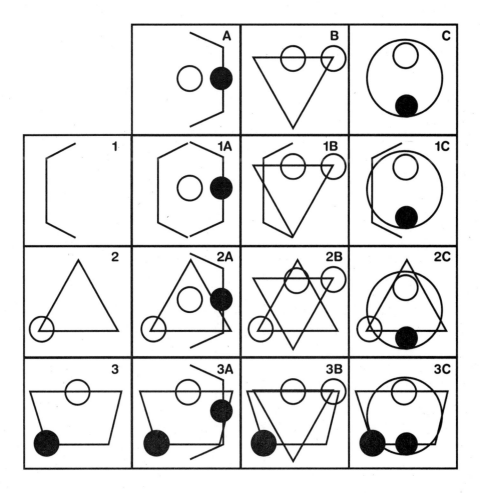

Answer see page 360

Puzzle 4

Which of the following has the same meaning as MENDICANT?

A. CHURCH OFFICIAL

B. REPAIRER

C. TEACHER

D. BEGGAR

E. CHEMIST

Puzzle 5

How many squares are there in this diagram?

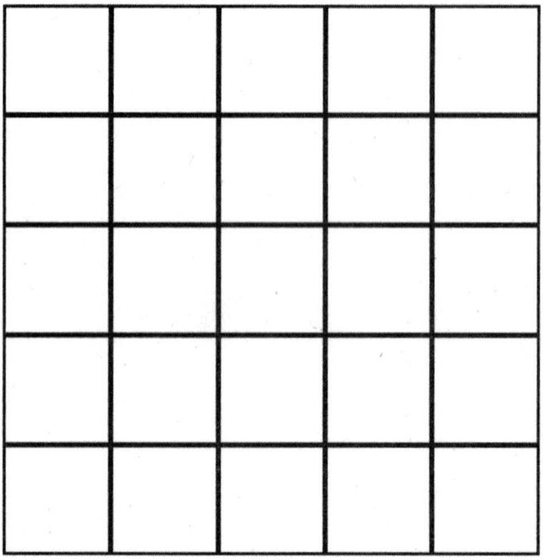

Answers see page 360

Puzzle 6

Complete the analogy.

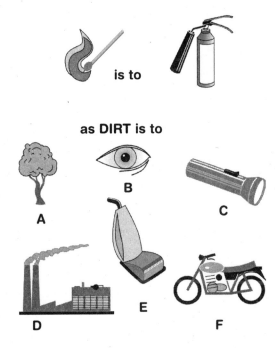

Puzzle 7

Two words using the same letters in their construction can be used to replace the dots in this sentence. The sentence will then make sense. Each dot is one letter. What are the words?

IN THE FOREST AS THE FRUIT •••••• THE

FURTIVE •••••• LURKS IN ANTICIPATION OF

HIS VICTIM.

Answers see page 361

Puzzle 8

Arrange the tiles in this diagram so that they form a square. When this is done correctly five words can be read down and across. What are the words?

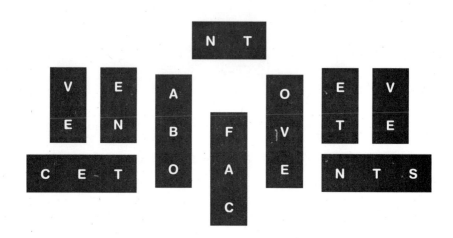

Puzzle 9 – Sudoku

7			2			5		
				1	8	4		
				6			3	
		6			9	1		7
				4				
2		8	7			6		
	6				8			
		4	6	3				
		3			2			4

Answers see page 361

Puzzle 10

Fill the numbers into the grid. They only fit one way.

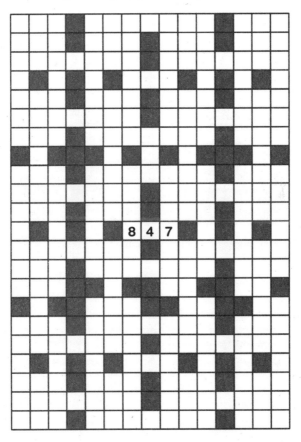

ACROSS

69	263	726	1761670
76	328	751	4256701
84	338	758	4971467
97	447	778	5231937
092	450	821	6368906
096	472	847	6579804
101	517	930	6596817
122	627	957	7062502
131	650	974	7554403
147	660	0379304	8369591
167	692	1062387	9511198
171	697	1291762	9512209
178	706	1518117	9974515
239	711	1751171	

DOWN

069	298915	1028507	7081701
106	412961	1508171	7097230
352	497811	1970788	7097429
353	517268	2567039	7121176
379	576816	3374277	7364561
461	584605	3602976	7607138
513	709656	4298164	7632154
573	720412	4650786	7948137
590	797991	5247127	8076467
126959	862178	7057147	9912061
162717			

Answer see page 362

Puzzle 11

When old gardener Lincoln died, he left his grandchildren 19 rose bushes each. The grandchildren, Agnes (A), Billy (B), Catriona (C) and Derek (D), hated each other, and so decided to fence off their plots as shown. Who had to build the greatest run of fence?

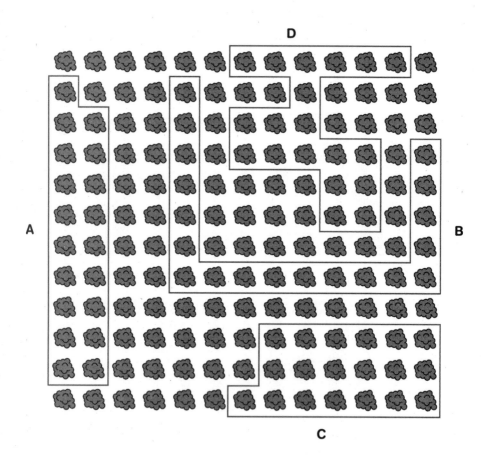

Puzzle 12

Which of these shapes is the odd one out?

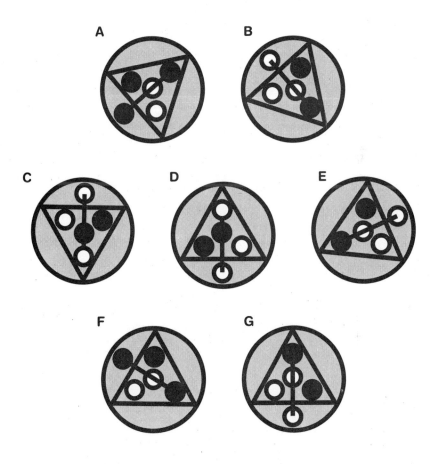

Answer see page 363

Puzzle 13

Which of the constructed boxes can be made from the pattern?

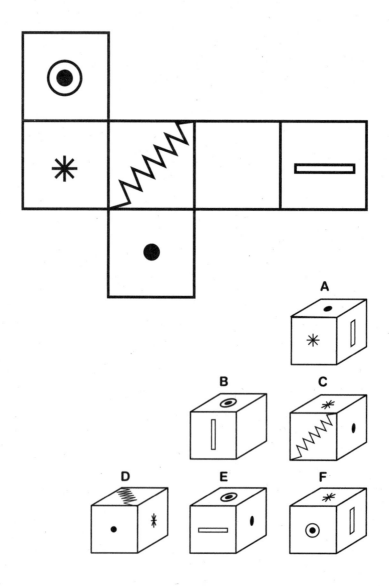

Answer see page 363

Puzzle 14

Insert the rows into the appropriate places in the grid to make all lines, columns, and long diagonals add to 105.

27	25	16

-2	-4	36

14	5	8

18	9	0

2	-7	33

-6	34	32

35	26	24	15	6	4	-5

Central grid column (middle): 39, 31, 23, 15, 7, -1, -9

19	17	8

38	29	20

-3	37	28

10	1	-8

22	13	11

30	21	12

Answer see page 363

Puzzle 15 – Sudoku

	5			3			8	
			2	7	5			
		2				7		
	9	8				2	1	
				9				
5		7				4		6
		4		2		8		
1				8				7
			5		1			

Puzzle 16

How many kangaroos are in this herd?

Answers see page 364

Puzzle 17

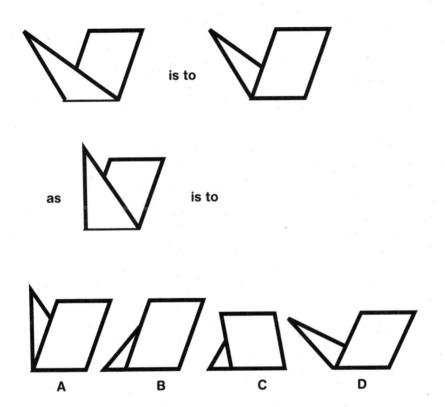

is to

as   is to

A   B   C   D

Answer see page 364

Puzzle 18

Which of the slices should be used to complete the cake?

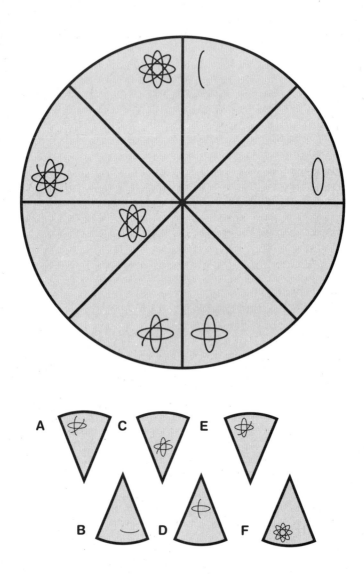

Answer see page 364

Puzzle 19

Look at the three squares. Does option A, B, C, D, E or F continue the sequence?

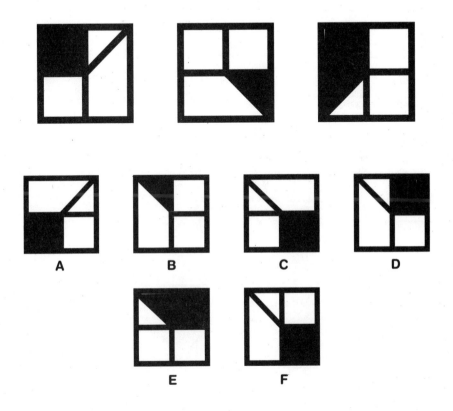

Answer see page 365

Puzzle 20

Which of the following will replace the question mark and complete the series?

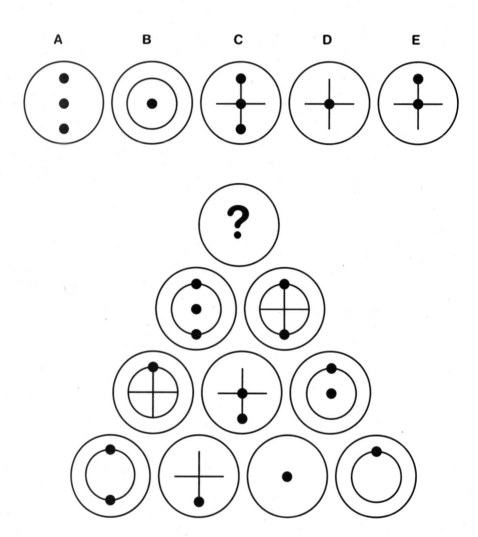

Answer see page 365

Puzzle 21

Place the letters shown into the diagram in such a way that three words can be read across and one down the middle. What are the words?

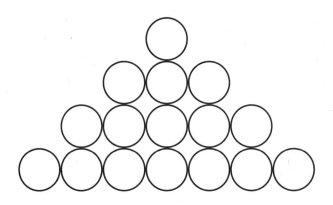

A A A B C D D E H I K L M N R Y

Puzzle 22 – Sudoku

7		1						6
6					8	4		
	8	2				9		
				9				
5			1	4	6			8
			7					
		7				2	1	
		4	6					5
1						8		4

Answers see page 365

Puzzle 23

Jim sat in the bedroom morosely watching the never-ending rain. It had fallen on his home town for three weeks without ceasing and there were now floods everywhere.

In most places the water was several feet deep and rising rapidly. Everyone had been forced to live upstairs. Just then his wife walked in but, try as he might, Jim couldn't get her to take the situation seriously.

Why not?

Puzzle 24

Old Silas Greenfield died and left each of his grandchildren the same bequest. Sam spent all his having a good time, Dave wasted his and Suzy used hers wisely.

The old man had been determined to treat the grandchildren equally, and in a way he did, but each got a different sum of money.

Why?

Answers see page 366

Puzzle 25

What is it that you can see with the naked eye, seems to have no weight and yet the more of them you put into an empty container, the lighter the container becomes?

Two answers are possible.

Puzzle 26

Two mothers and two daughters went shopping for new dresses for a wedding celebration. They each returned with a new dress, but they had only bought 3 dresses.

How can this be correct?

Answers see page 366

Puzzle 27

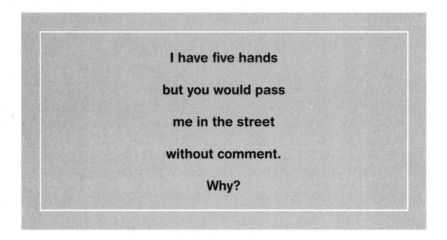

I have five hands

but you would pass

me in the street

without comment.

Why?

Puzzle 28

What number should replace the question mark?

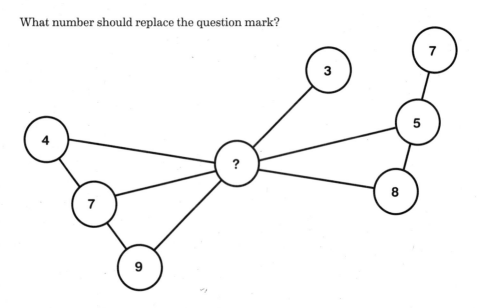

Answers see page 367

Puzzle 1

Move from circle to touching circle, starting from the bottom left corner and finishing in the top right corner. A red circle is worth minus 3, a blue one minus 1 and a green one minus 2. Collect nine circles each time and total them. How many different routes are there to total 0?

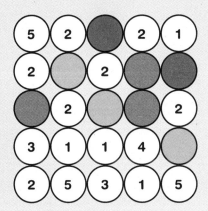

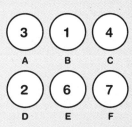

Puzzle 2

Find a number that could replace the question mark.

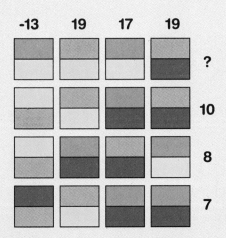

Answers see page 240

Puzzle 3

Would you put the pink smiley in column 1 or column 2?

Puzzle 4

Orange is the odd one out. Why?

Answers see page 240

Puzzle 5

The hues on the sphere are a clue to the word. The second part of each word begins with the letter given and has one letter per blank shown. What are the words?

Puzzle 6

When the square is completed no two identical squares will appear in any row, column or diagonal line. What should replace the question mark?

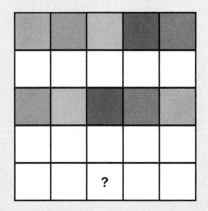

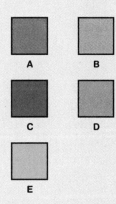

Answers see page 240

Puzzle 7

Place the shape over the grid so that no colour appears twice in the same row or column. Beware, the shape may not be the right way up!

Puzzle 8

Can you crack the colour code and make your way from one red square to the other? Each colour takes you up, down, left or right. The blue arrow tells you which way is up.

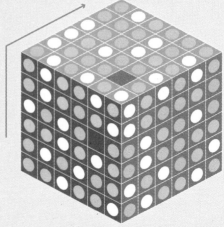

Answers see page 240

Puzzle 9

This square is drawn according to a certain logic. If you can work out what the system is you should be able to fill in the missing area.

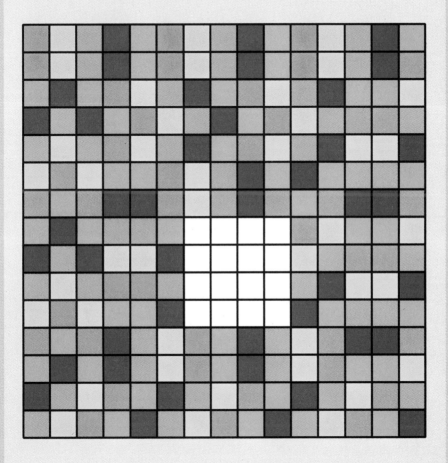

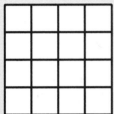

Answer see page 240

Puzzle 10

Which of these shapes is the odd one out?

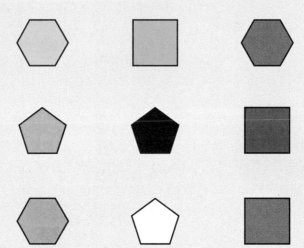

Puzzle 11

Does pink go above or below the line?

Answers see page 240

Puzzle 12

2	3	3	1	4	1
A	B	C	D	E	F

Here is an unusual safe. Each of the buttons must be pressed only once in the correct order to open it. The last button is marked F. The number of moves is marked on each button. A pink number means move down. A blue number means move up. A green number means move left and a red number means move right. Thus a blue 1 would mean one move up, whilst a green 1 would mean one move to the left. Which button is the first you must press?

2	3	6	3	1	2
5	3	1	3	1	2
2	1	F	3	1	3
4	1	2	2	1	3
5	1	3	1	2	2
2	1	1	5	3	5
1	6	4	1	1	2

Puzzle 13

Find a number that could replace the question mark. Each color represents a number under 10.

Answers see page 240

Puzzle 14

Fill the diagram up with circles. The black circle goes in the middle and represents the letter E. Yellow circles are Is, blue circles are Cs, and green circles are Ms. When the correct pattern has been found, by moving from circle to touching circle, including in diagonal leaps, and in each case ending at the black circle, the letters of the word MICE can be traced 25 times. What does the pattern look like?

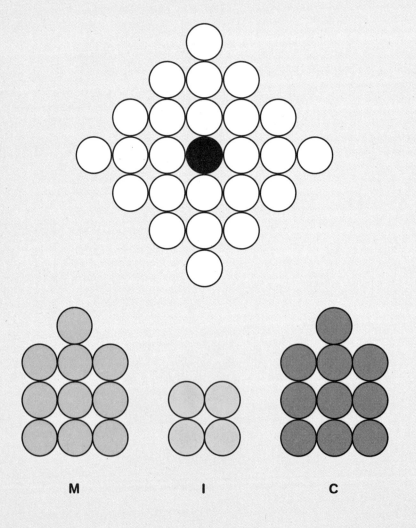

M   I   C

Answer see page 240

Puzzle 15

Find a number that could replace the question mark. Each color represents a number under 10.

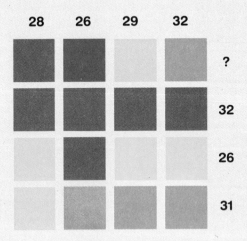

Puzzle 16

Make your way from A to B without passing through any pink squares – then do it again without passing through any purple squares!

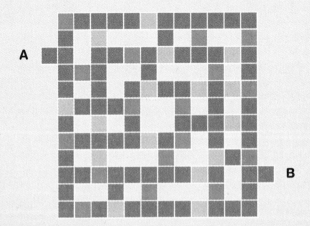

Answers see page 240

Puzzle 17

The following is a coded message. The only clue you get is that the answer is related to the colours used.

T	J	S	H	I	V
K	S	D	J	M	E
S	S	R	T	A	Z
G	E	L	I	S	A
H	M	I	Q	D	D
M	E	X	T	W	L
N	V	L	C	G	K

Puzzle 18

A yellow circle is worth 3, a red circle 4, a green one 5 and an orange one 2. Black circles are worth minus 2 each. Follow the arrows from the bottom left-hand circle to the top right-hand circle. Total the circles as you go. What is the highest you can total?

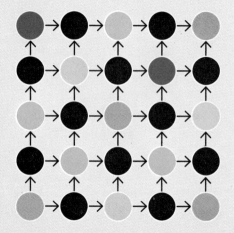

8	**6**
A	B
20	**12**
C	D
16	**10**
E	F

Answers see page 240

Puzzle 19

What is yellow worth?

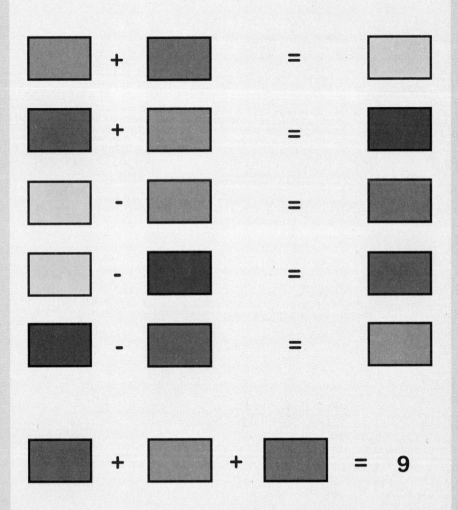

Answer see page 240

Puzzle 20

What colour replaces the question mark?

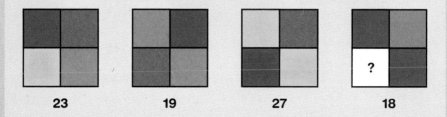

23   19   27   18

Puzzle 21

Which well known character is represented by this rebus?

boy

Answers see page 240

Puzzle 22

The word frame at the bottom is constructed from multi-tinted tiles. Choose a letter from the grid and insert it in the frame. The letter must be written on a matching tile. When the process has been completed a fictional character can be found. Who is it?

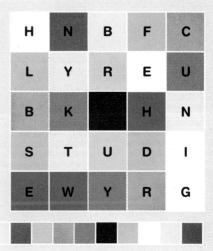

Puzzle 23

The grid below contains the name of a European country. To find it you must move from square to touching square (including diagonals). To help you, colours making up the name have something in common.

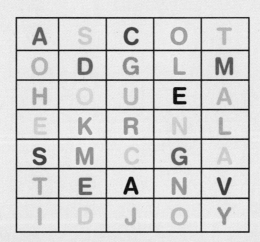

Answers see page 240

237

Puzzle 24

Each same box has a value. Work out the logic and discover what should replace the question mark.

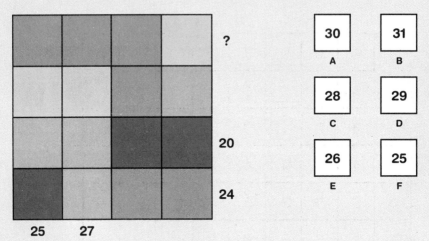

Puzzle 25

Which colour is the circle that replaces the question mark?

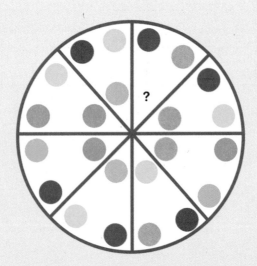

Answers see page 240

Puzzle 26

Find a number that could replace the question mark. Each color represents a number under 10.

3	4	6	9	7	2	5	8	3	9	?
6	5	2	7	3	4	5	1	2	6	71
3	8	2	1	9	7	8	6	1	3	82
5	4	3	4	1	2	9	8	6	5	85
6	8	9	3	5	4	8	3	6	2	91
4	1	9	8	6	3	2	2	4	5	74
7	6	3	5	2	4	6	8	9	7	93
8	4	6	5	3	6	2	1	3	8	83
9	2	1	4	3	7	8	9	6	3	88
1	3	7	6	4	3	8	6	2	4	77
89	75	77	87	83	86	81	93	67	102	

Answer see page 240

Solutions

1. B.

2. 17. The colours are worth: red 6, yellow 7, green 10, orange 12. In each square subtract the lower color from the upper.

3. Column 1. All the colours in column 1 have one syllable, all those in column 2 have two syllables.

4. It is the only one to start with a vowel.

5. Greenheart and blackheart

6. A.

7.

8.

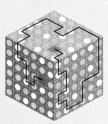

9.

The pattern follows a 5-colour sequence – orange, yellow, pink, green, red – spiralling inwards from the top left corner.

10. The red rectangle. In all the others the number of sides of the shape is the same as the number of letters in the colour.

11. Below, all those above have an initial B, those below have P.

12. F. Pink 1 in the third row, second column.

13. 77. The colours are worth: purple 3, green 4, yellow 6, orange 9. Add the left side to the right side and mutiply by the base to get Result 1. Add the two upper internal colours and subtract the lower to get Result 2. Then subtract R2 from R1 to get the total.

14.

15. 26. The colours are worth: red 3, yellow 6, orange 7, purple 8, green 9.

16.

17. 'This message is hidden.' Take only the letters that have no 'e' in name of the colour.

18. F.

19. 7. Red is worth 2, green 3, blue 4 and purple 5.

20. Yellow. Green is worth 3, red 4, yellow 7 and blue 9.

21. Little boy blue.

22. Huckleberry Finn.

23. Germany. The colours all have five-letter names.

24. D. Green is worth 6, red 4, pink 7 and yellow 8.

25. Yellow. The colours are worth: pink 2, yellow 3, orange 4, green 5, purple 6, red 7, brown 8. In each segment subtract the smaller of the outer numbers from the larger and put the result in the centre of the next segment clockwise.

26. 96. The colours are worth: pink 2, yellow 3, green 4, orange 5.

Puzzle 29

Each row has numbers going +3, -2, +3, and each column has numbers going -3, +2, -3. Place all the numbered pieces in to the grid to fulfil these criteria.

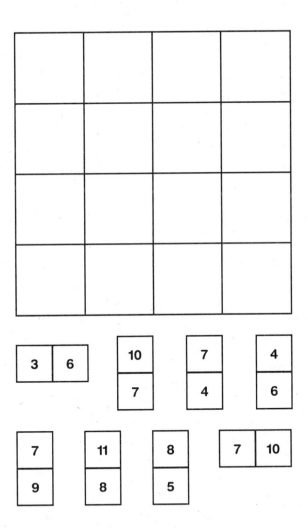

Answer see page 367

Puzzle 30

Starting at the top number and travelling down one level each time until you reach the bottom number, what is the highest number you can achieve.

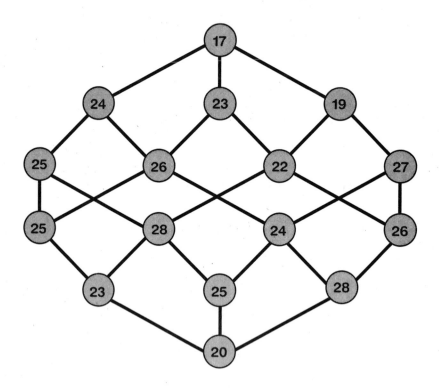

Answer see page 367

Puzzle 31 – Sudoku

3			2			7		
	4				9	2		
	7		4					6
8	3						9	
				5				
	5						2	3
7					4		6	
		4	1				5	
		8			7			1

Puzzle 32

What word can be placed in front of the other five to form five new words? Each dot represents a letter.

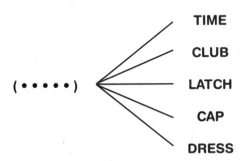

(• • • • •)
TIME
CLUB
LATCH
CAP
DRESS

Answers see page 368

Puzzle 33

The symbols in the following calculations represent the numbers from 0 to 9. Each like symbol always represents the same number. What symbol should replace the question mark?

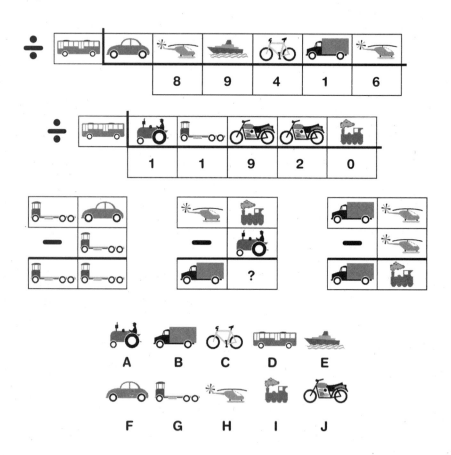

Answer see page 368

Puzzle 34

What word will go with the following series?

GAMMON   ACHE   TRACK   ?

A. MEAT

B. WARD

C. FIND

D. SMOOTH

E. KIND

Puzzle 35 – Sudoku

		1		4	3	7		
7				9			2	
							1	4
	1							2
	3		8		5			
9							7	
3	6							
	4			3				5
		7	9	6		3		

Answers see page 369

Puzzle 36

Place one letter in the middle of this diagram. Four five-letter words can now be arranged from each straight line of letters. What is the letter and what are the words?

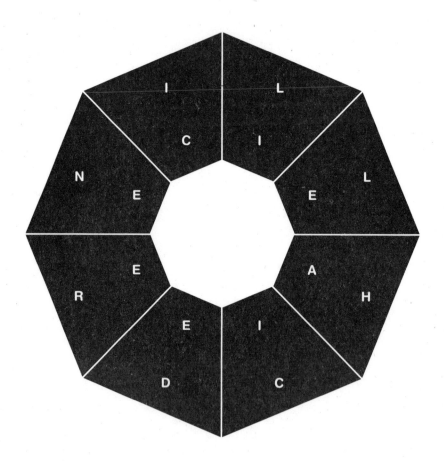

Answer see page 369

Puzzle 37

No sign is used on more than one side of the box. Which of these is not a view of the same box?

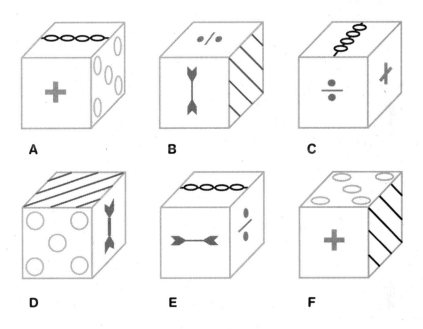

A   **B**   **C**

D   **E**   **F**

Answer see page 369

Puzzle 38

Which of the constructed boxes cannot be made from the pattern?

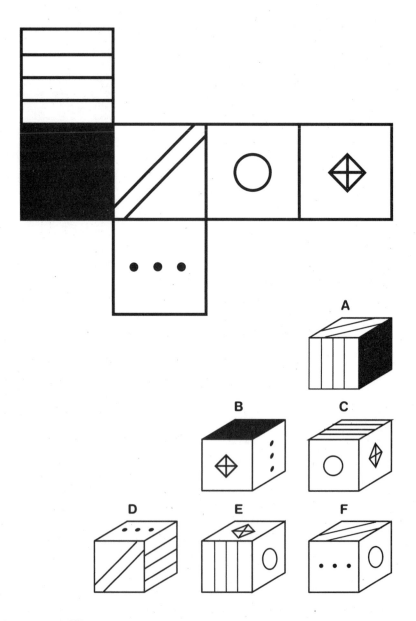

Answer see page 370

Puzzle 39

What number replaces the question mark?

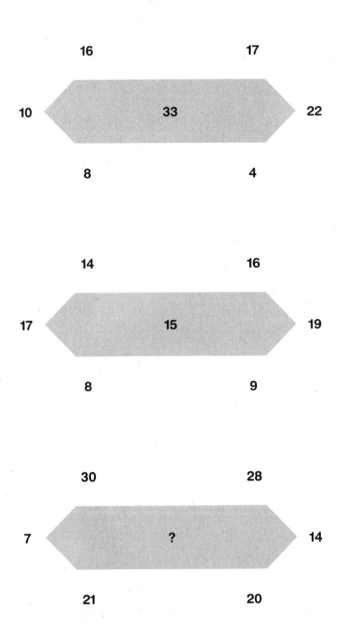

Answer see page 370

Puzzle 40

How many cobras are in this menacing group?

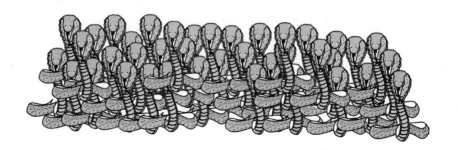

Puzzle 41 – Sudoku

			3		1			
6								3
	1						2	
			7					
	2		9				1	
	9		2	3	4		8	
7		8				4		6
			5		7			
		4				7		

Answers see page 370

Puzzle 42

Which of the following is the odd one out?

A. CASKET

B. CARBOY

C. DECANTER

D. DEMIJOHN

E. AMPULLA

Puzzle 43

Which anagrammed book title is the odd one out?

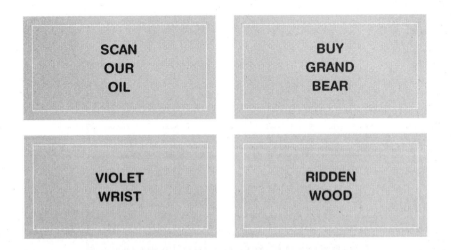

SCAN OUR OIL	BUY GRAND BEAR
VIOLET WRIST	RIDDEN WOOD

Answers see page 371

Puzzle 44

Five of the words in the diagram are associated for some reason. Find the words
and then work out whether WIDOW belongs to the group.

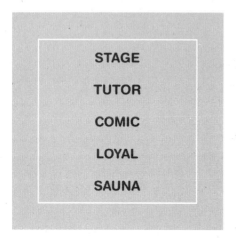

STAGE

TUTOR

COMIC

LOYAL

SAUNA

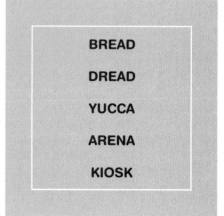

BREAD

DREAD

YUCCA

ARENA

KIOSK

Puzzle 45

A life prisoner appealed to the king for pardon. Not being ready to grant the appeal
the king proposed a pardon on condition that the prisoner should start from cell A
and go in and out of each cell in the prison, coming back to cell A without going in
any cell twice. How could it be done?

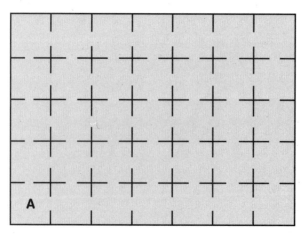

Answers see page 371

Puzzle 46

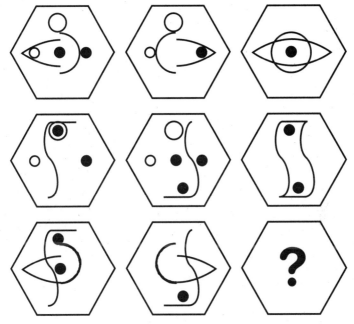

Which of the hexagons below should replace the question mark above?

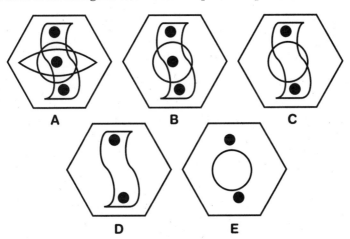

Answer see page 372

Puzzle 47

Which hexagon replaced the question mark?

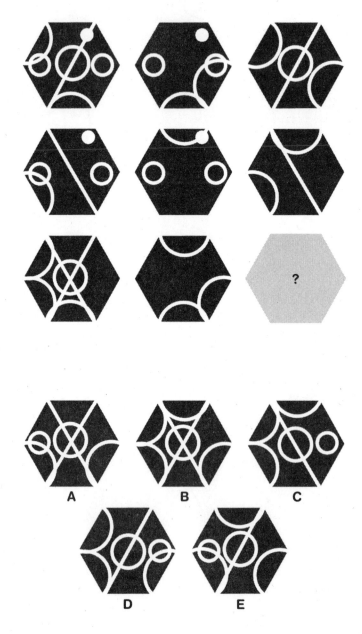

Answer see page 372

Puzzle 48

Which of the following is the odd one out?

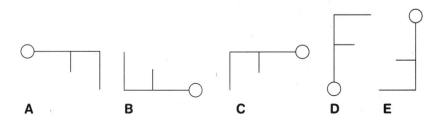

Puzzle 49

Which of these is not an anagram of currency?

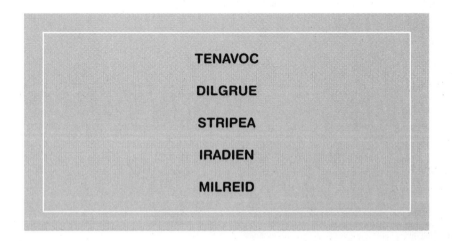

TENAVOC

DILGRUE

STRIPEA

IRADIEN

MILREID

Answers see page 372

Puzzle 50 – Sudoku

	1				7			9
9			4				1	
			2					8
	6	7	5			4		
				7				
4						2		6
			9		1			5
	5						3	
7		3			5	1		

Puzzle 51

Which shape is missing from this series?

Puzzle 52

Which shield, below, will replace the question mark below?

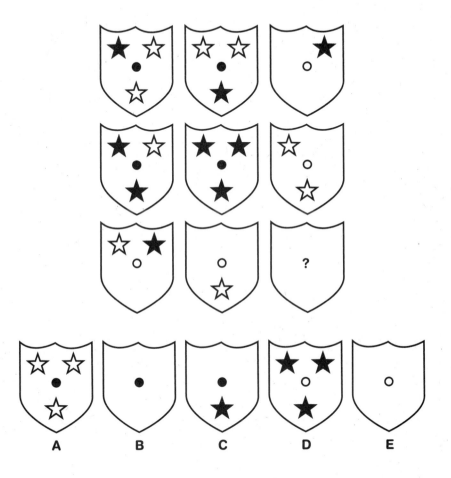

Answer see page 373

Puzzle 53

Find the only route from the perimeter of this field to the shaded path around the diamond.

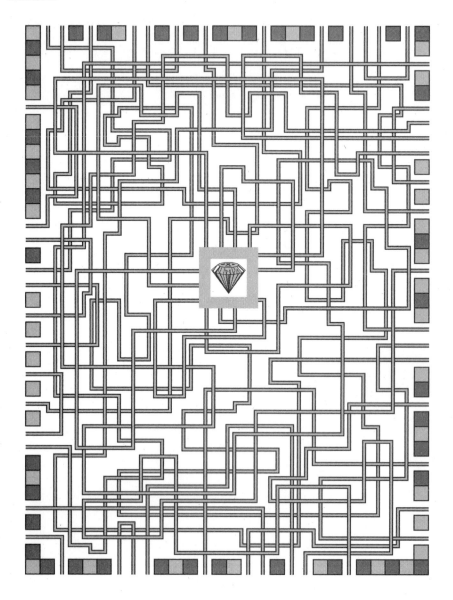

Answer see page 374

Puzzle 54

What number comes next?

11, 24, 39, 416, 525,

?

Puzzle 55

A man writes a check and then tears it into 185 pieces and posts it to a department store.

Why did he do that?

Answers see page 375

Puzzle 56

How many times do the 10 letters 'QWERTYUIOP' appear in a straight line in any order. All 10 letters must be uninterrupted by other letters. They can appear horizontally, vertically, diagonally, backwards or forwards.

```
P  S  Q  T  R  Y  E  W  U  P  O  Q  I  C  D
O  V  Q  W  T  W  M  Q  O  T  K  W  L  S  W
I  X  P  Q  E  P  O  I  U  Y  T  E  W  R  Q
Y  V  O  U  C  T  U  A  V  D  B  R  N  H  O
U  Y  I  W  X  Y  R  K  R  P  E  T  Y  O  P
R  P  W  E  T  B  M  Y  P  B  J  Y  V  I  E
T  Q  U  R  E  A  E  R  U  U  F  U  C  U  I
W  O  E  T  Z  J  G  Z  F  I  W  I  P  P  R
E  W  Y  Y  N  P  Q  C  F  C  O  O  M  Y  U
Q  E  R  I  R  T  E  Y  U  W  I  P  O  Q  T
U  R  T  O  Q  P  I  W  T  Y  U  E  R  T  Y
J  T  A  P  Q  O  W  E  R  T  I  Y  U  R  E
S  Y  R  C  Q  I  U  O  P  Y  T  W  Q  E  R
P  I  O  P  U  Q  W  E  Y  T  R  X  V  W  K
J  U  D  X  D  V  B  D  S  L  K  J  Z  K  N
```

Answer see page 375

Puzzle 57

Find a six-letter word made up of only the following four letters?

Puzzle 58

Complete the word ladder by changing one letter of each word per step. The newly created word must be found in the dictionary.

What are the words to turn DROP to FALL?

Answers see page 375-6

Puzzle 59

When rearranged the shapes will give a letter. Which of the letters is it?

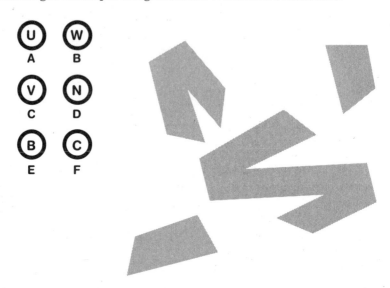

A. U
B. W
C. V
D. N
E. B
F. C

Puzzle 60 – Sudoku

					2			6
			8		1	5		
		2	6		7		4	
	8	6					7	
				4				
2	5	7						9
	6						9	
		9	1			2		
1					6			

Answers see page 376

Puzzle 61

Divide these two grids into SIX identical shapes each. The sum of the numbers in each section must give the total shown.

Total 100

18	6	4	30	47	29
45	30	6	18	17	2
1	21	1	42	23	5
3	28	7	17	1	6
44	4	32	43	30	40

Total 18

6	2	3	4	4	3
3	5	5	2	6	2
5	3	1	3	5	0
2	4	5	3	0	5
3	3	4	6	6	5

Answer see page 376

Puzzle 62

Select one of the two letters from the grid, in accordance with the reference shown, and place it in the word frame. When the correct letters have been chosen a sixteen-letter word can be read.

What is the word?

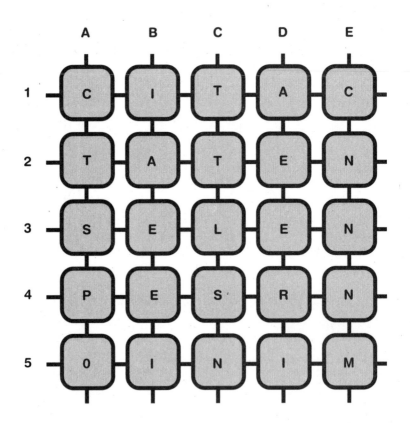

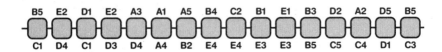

Answer see page 377

Puzzle 63

Divide the grid into four equal segments. Each segment must contain the same symbols, that is three of each: triangle, circle, diamond.

Answer see page 377

Puzzle 64

Change the first letter of each word to the left and to the right. Two other English words must be formed. Place the letter used in the empty section. When this has been completed, for all the words, another English word can be read down.

What is the word?

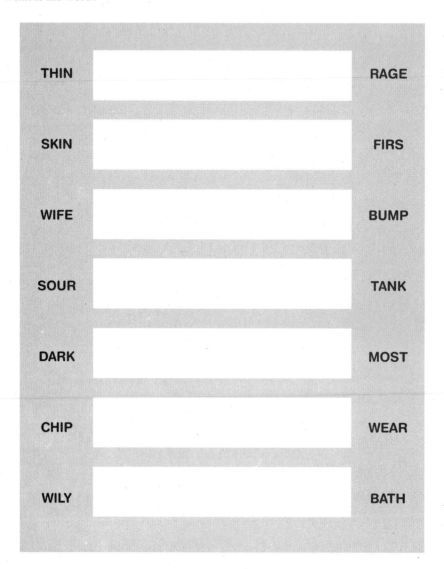

THIN		RAGE
SKIN		FIRS
WIFE		BUMP
SOUR		TANK
DARK		MOST
CHIP		WEAR
WILY		BATH

Answer see page 377

Puzzle 65

Here is a piece of land marked off with 36 circular plots, on each of which is deposited a bag containing as many gold coins as the figures indicated in the diagram. You are allowed to pick up as many bags as you like, provided that you do not take two lying on the same line.

What is the largest amount of money you can pick up?

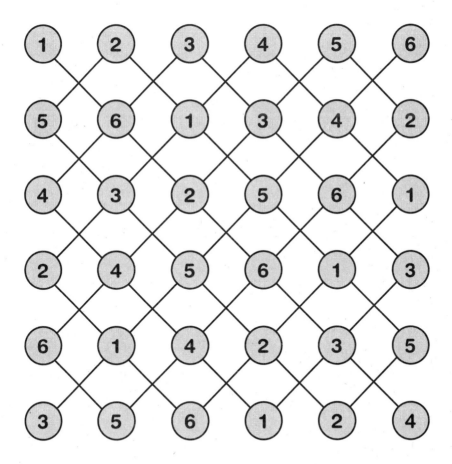

Answer see page 378

Puzzle 66 – Sudoku

	3			9				
6			3		8		7	2
4						9		
					9			
5		9		4		3		8
			7					
		7						3
8	2		6		1			5
				7			6	

Puzzle 67

A committee of 6 is to be formed from a group of seven men and four women. How many different committees can be formed if at least 2 women are included?

Answers see page 378

Puzzle 68

Place the letters shown into the diagram in such a way that three words can be read across and one down the middle. What are the words?

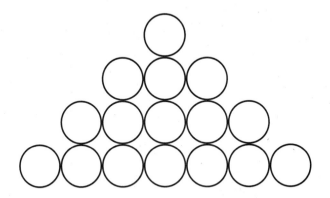

A A A B C E E E H M M M R T T Z

Puzzle 69

Should A, B, C, or D fill the empty circle?

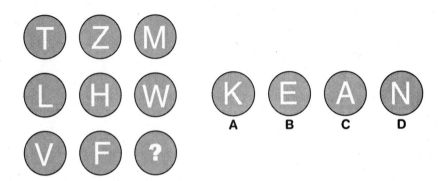

Answers see page 378-9

Puzzle 70

Which of the following will replace the question mark and complete the series?

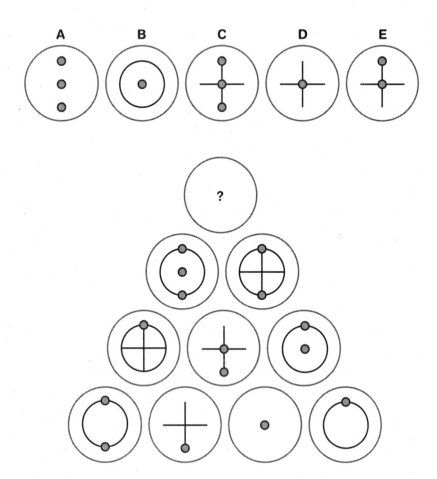

Answer see page 379

Puzzle 71

Which of these boxes can be made from the template? Is it A, B, C, D, E, or F?

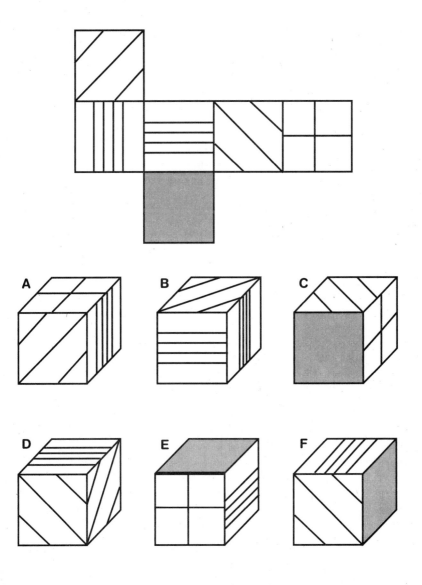

Answer see page 379

Puzzle 72

Complete the square using the five symbols shown. When completed no row, column or diagonal line will use the same symbol more than once.

What should replace the question mark?

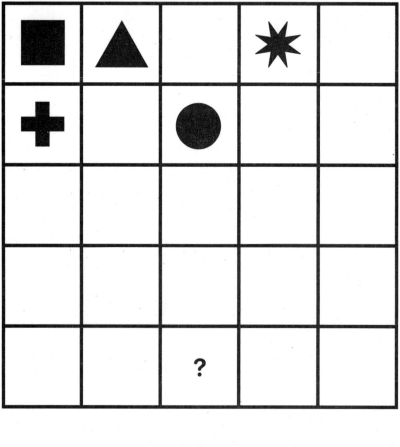

A

B

C

D

E

Answer see page 379

Puzzle 1

This is a simple coded message that depends on colours for its solution.

```
T  X  B  Q  H
M  K  I  S  D
R  O  N  E  S
I  S  G  A  B
I  X  B  T  E
F  H  G  A  L
R  D  P  D  L
J  P  E  R  S
```

Puzzle 2

Find the missing number.

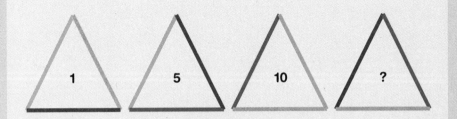

Answers see page 288

Puzzle 3

Three reptiles can be found in the diagram. The letters are written in the correct order. Only three different shades of letter are used in each name. What are they?

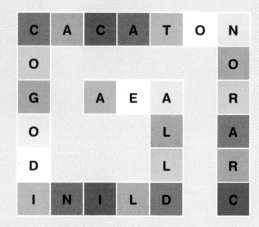

Puzzle 4

Which of the constructed boxes can be made from the pattern?

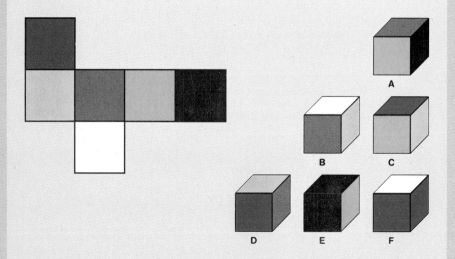

Answers see page 288

Puzzle 5

Find a number that could replace the question mark. Each colour represents a number under 10.

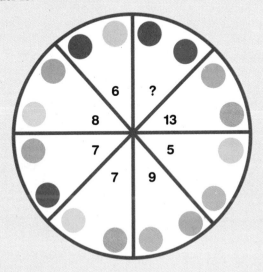

Puzzle 6

What does this rebus represent?

JUICE

Answers see page 288

Puzzle 7

Find a number that could replace the question mark. Each colour represents a number under 10.

4	8	3	2	7	5	6	1	9	4	?
2	3	7	6	2	4	1	5	3	7	90
8	7	3	2	4	6	9	1	4	2	101
4	3	6	8	2	9	7	6	8	7	115
3	2	1	6	9	8	8	7	3	4	101
6	2	3	8	4	1	9	7	2	6	104
7	3	4	2	1	9	4	5	3	5	100
6	5	4	3	2	8	4	7	6	1	103
3	5	2	1	8	6	9	4	3	7	106
6	8	7	3	2	4	5	9	5	6	109

103 98 99 100 81 117 121 109 99 107

Answer see page 288

Puzzle 8

Move from circle to touching circle, starting from the bottom left corner and finishing in the top right corner. Collect nine circles each time. How many different routes are there to collect two orange, two pink, two green, two yellow and one black?

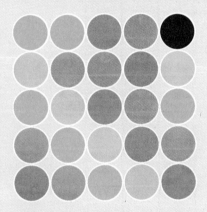

9	6	13
A	B	C

15	12	10
D	E	F

Puzzle 9

The values of the segments are 3 consecutive numbers under 10. The yellow is worth 7 and the sum of the segments equals 50. What do the blue and green segments equal?

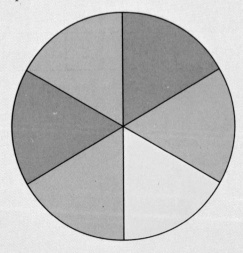

Answers see page 288

Puzzle 10

The hues on the sphere are a clue to the word. The second part of each word begins with the letter given and has one letter per blank shown. What are the words?

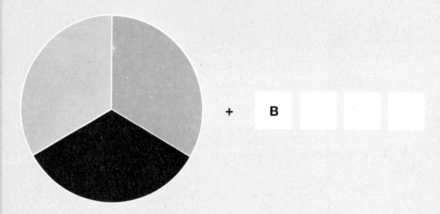

+ B ▯ ▯ ▯

Puzzle 11

These colours and shapes all have a numerical significance. Once you work out what it is you will be able to find the missing number.

Answers see page 288

Puzzle 12

When the square is completed no two identical squares will appear in any row, column or diagonal line. What should replace the question mark?

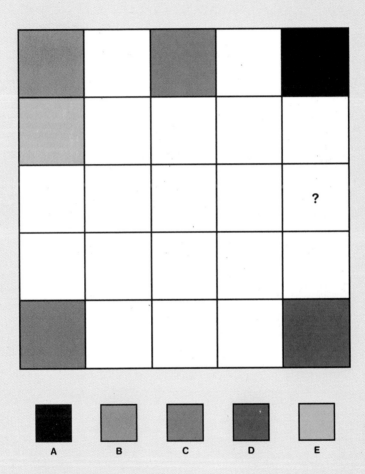

Answer see page 288

Puzzle 13

Find a number that could replace the question mark. Each colour represents a number under 10.

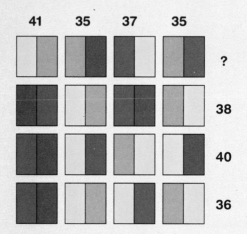

Puzzle 14

Which circle is missing from this series?

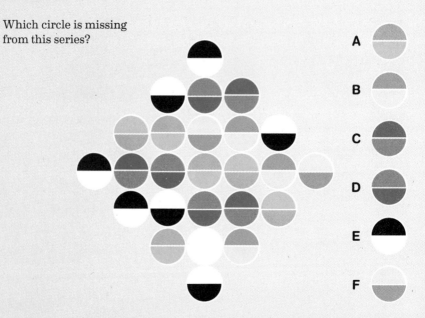

Answers see page 288

Puzzle 15

Each same box has a value. Work out the logic and discover what should replace the question mark.

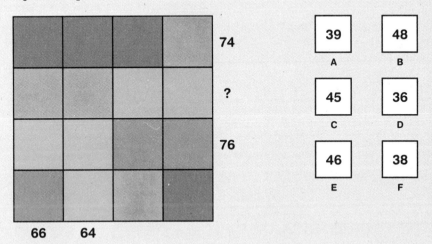

74

?

76

66   64

A	B
39	48

C	D
45	36

E	F
46	38

Puzzle 16

Find a number that could replace the question mark. Each colour represents a number under 10.

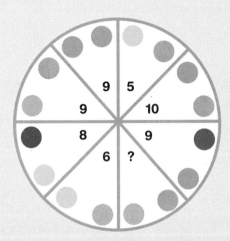

Answers see page 288

Puzzle 17

The small squares form a logical sequence. If you can discover what that sequence is you should be able to complete the missing section.

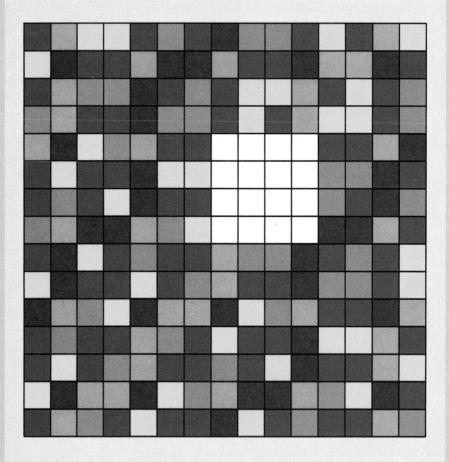

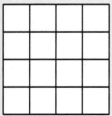

Answer see page 288

Puzzle 18

Complete the grid so that every row and column contains one red, orange and green dot. The dots at the end of each row and column tell you the colour of the first dot you will meet traveling in that direction along that row or down that column.

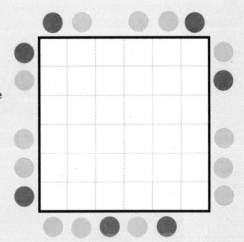

Puzzle 19

Start at any corner and follow the lines. Collect another four boxes. Green boxes are worth 4 each, pink boxes are worth 2, yellow boxes are worth 3 and dark blue boxes are worth 5. Total the five boxes. What is the highest possible total?

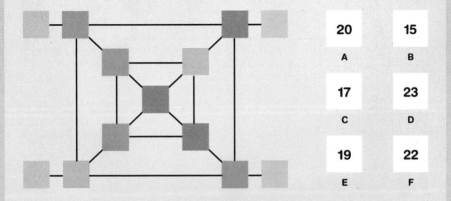

20	**15**
A	B
17	**23**
C	D
19	**22**
E	F

Answers see page 288

Puzzle 20

Three of the patterns are a flat view of the picture below. Can you find the three that do not match?

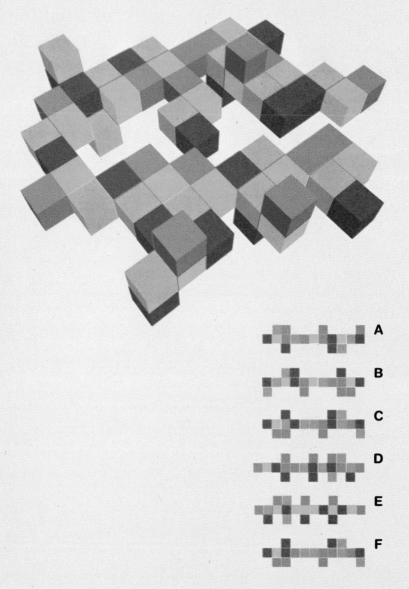

A

B

C

D

E

F

Answer see page 288

Puzzle 21

Find a number that could replace the question mark. Each colour represents a number under 10.

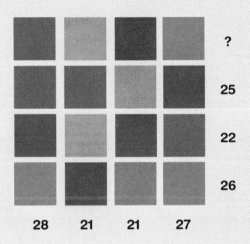

?
25
22
26

28   21   21   27

Puzzle 22

Does white belong with group A or B?

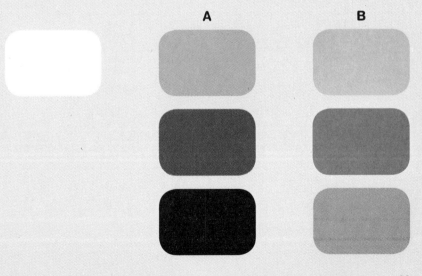

A   B

Answers see page 288

Puzzle 23

Fill the diagram up with circles. The black circle goes in the middle and represents the letter W. Red circles are Ss, blue circles are Is, and yellow circles are Es. When the correct pattern has been found, by moving from circle to touching circle, including with internal diagonal leaps, and in each case starting at the black circle, the letters of the word WISE can be traced 21 times. What does the pattern look like?

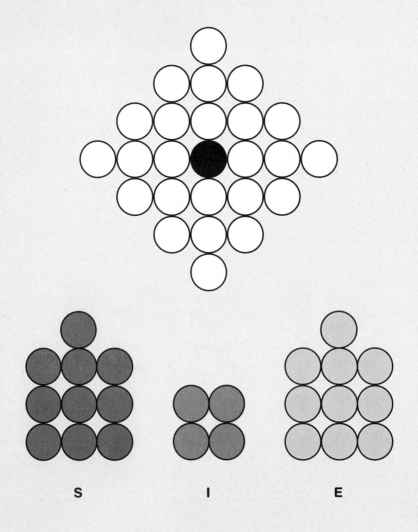

S   I   E

Answer see page 288

Puzzle 24

The letters conceal a well-known phrase from a Shakespearean play. The letters of each word are the same colour, though they have been mixed up. Letters of other colours have been introduced to add confusion.

```
W    T    T    D    J
A    S    H    M    H
U    O    G    A    I
E    T    L    E    R
T    E    W    O    D
O    F    H    U    T
O    R    H    S    P
R    O    A    Y    O
E    D    I    A    M
R    P    E    J    H
```

Puzzle 25

Find a number that could replace the question mark.

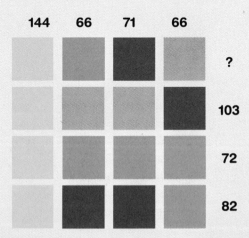

	144	66	71	66	
					?
					103
					72
					82

Answers see page 288

Solutions

1. If you take only the colours with five letters in their name (green and brown), you get, 'This one is a bit harder'.

2. 7. The colours are worth: green 4, purple 5, red 6, orange 8. The formula is left side plus base, minus right side.

3. Crocodile, alligator and anadonda.

4. B.

5. 11. The colours are worth: green 2, orange 3, yellow 4, pink 5, red 6, purple 7. Add the outer numbers in each segment and place in the center of the next segment clockwise.

6. Orange juice.

7. 105. The colours are worth: yellow 4, pink 5, green 6, orange 7. Add the value of the color to the number in each square.

8. D.

9. Blue = 8; Green = 9.

10. Blackbird, bluebird and yellowbird.

11. 149. All colours have their alphanumeric value. A smiley face means subtract 20, a heart means subtract 15, a crossed circle means subtract 10, a star means subtract 5. The value of each row is added and the total placed at the end.

12. B.

13. 34. The colours are worth: green 3, red 4, yellow 5, purple 7. Add colours in each square together.

14. F. Start in the top circle. The series moves across from left to right as follows: black/white, white/black, blue/red, red/blue, green/orange, orange/green etc...

15. E. Blue is worth 23, orange 5, green 18 and pink 20.

16. 6. The colours are worth: yellow 1, green 3, pink 4, orange 5, red 6, purple 9. Add the outer numbers and put the result in the opposite segment.

17.

The sequence is brown, orange, yellow, brown, purple, green. It forms a diagonal boustrophedon (or ox plough pattern) starting in the bottom left corner.

18.

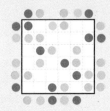

19. F.

20. A, D and F are not views.

21. 24. The colours are worth: orange 4, red 5, green 7, purple 8.

22. Group B. All the colours in Group B have an E in them, none of the As do.

23.

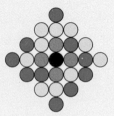

24. The red, black, green and orange letters spell out, 'Wherefore art thou Romeo'.

25. 90. Colours are worth: orange 25, purple 17, yellow 36, green 12.

Puzzle 73

A quotation has been written in this diagram. Find the start letter and move from square to touching square until you have found it.

What is the quotation and to whom is it attributed?

O	D	L	L	H	S	I	G
D	O	C	A	T	T	H	N
D	R	A	T	O	S	A	I
I	E	E	R	T	T	E	L
M	Y	D	H	A	S	T	H

Answer see page 380

Puzzle 74

Which of these boxes can be made from the template?

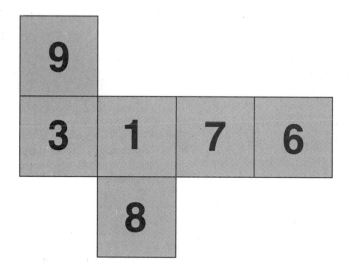

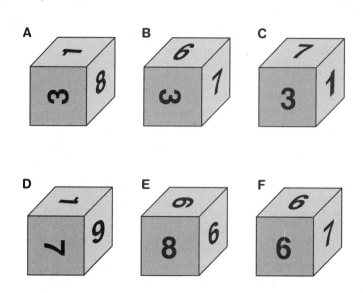

Answer see page 380

Puzzle 75

Which arrow is missing from this series?

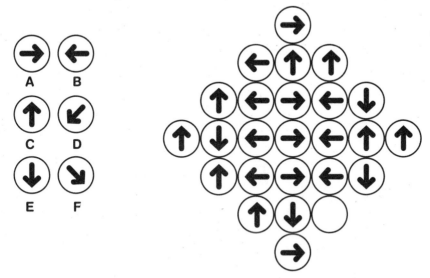

A   B

C   D

E   F

Puzzle 76

Which word is the odd one out?

ODE   ICE   TOILED   ORDAIN   RADIAL

OAR   NEARER   CIRCLE   USE   AIL   OLD

POODLE   ACT   ERR   RAN   MOHAIR   PURSUE

Answers see page 380

Puzzle 77

Insert the numbers 0–8 in the circles, so that for any particular circle, the sum of the numbers in the circles connected directly to it, equals the value corresponding to the number in the circle in the following list:

0 = 16, 1 = 13, 2 = 6, 3= 0, 4 = 6, 5 = 7, 6 = 7, 7 = 14. 8 = 7

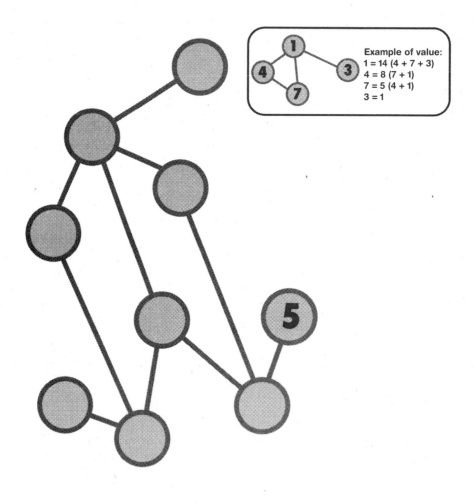

Example of value:
1 = 14 (4 + 7 + 3)
4 = 8 (7 + 1)
7 = 5 (4 + 1)
3 = 1

Answer see page 381

Puzzle 78

The caseload of books arrived with some very strange messages written on the sides. Actually one of the messages is an anagram of the book contained within the case and it's author. Can you work out what book is inside the case?

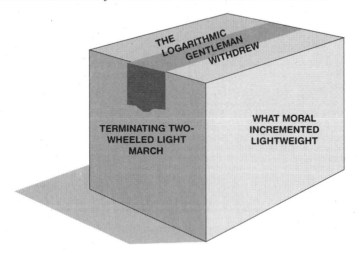

Puzzle 79

Two words using the same letters in their construction can be used to replace the dots in this sentence. The sentence will then make sense. Each dot is one letter. What are the words?

THE VALUABLE SCIENTIFIC EQUIPMENT WAS

CAREFULLY •••••• AND CHECKED BEFORE

BEING •••••• TO THE OTHER SIDE OF

THE BUILDING.

Answers see page 381

Puzzle 80

What word is the odd one out?

A. REGENERATE

B. REGURGITATE

C. REVITALIZE

D. RESUSCITATE

E. REANIMATE

Puzzle 81 – Sudoku

6								4
	5				9	8		
				3	5	7		
		3		6		2	8	
8		2		9	4			
	8			4	2			
		1					2	
5				1				8

Answers see page 381-2

Puzzle 82

Here is an unusual safe. Each of the buttons must be pressed only once in the correct order to open it. The last button is marked F. The number of moves and the direction is marked on each button. Thus 1U would mean one move up, while 1L would mean one move to the left. Using the grid reference, which button is the first you must press?

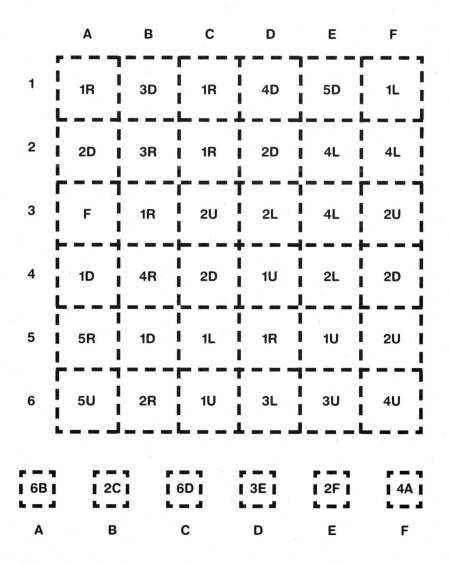

Answer see page 382

Puzzle 83

The diagram shows the sunshine hours in England for four months. The numbers bear a relationship to the letters in the words. What should replace the question mark?

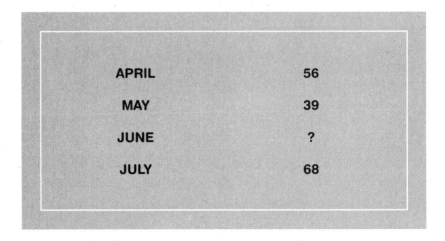

APRIL	56
MAY	39
JUNE	?
JULY	68

Puzzle 84

DREY is to SQUIRREL as HOLT is to:

A. OTTER

B. BADGER

C. BOAR

D. FERRET

E. MOLE

Answers see page 382

Puzzle 85

The numbers in the left-hand box move clockwise around the square to the positions shown in the box on the right. In which positions should the missing numbers appear?

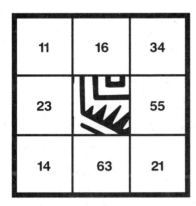

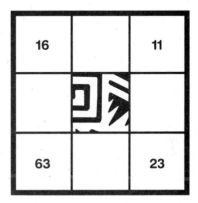

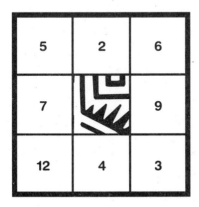

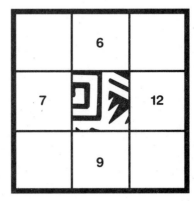

Answer see page 383

Puzzle 86 – Sudoku

			9		2	1	4	
		4		3				
	2							
3			6	7				
	8		2					9
6					4	7	2	
8					1	5		
1					9			3
			6				7	

Puzzle 87

I wanted to know the birthday of a work colleague, I knew it was during February but did not know the actual date. I asked six other colleagues. This is how they answered:

A said, "It is an odd number."
B said, "it is a prime number."
C said, "it is between 6 and 16."
D said, "it is before 10."
E said, "It is a double-digit number."
F said "it is between 8 and 12."

One of them had lied. What was the date? (1 is not considered to be a prime number).

Answers see page 383

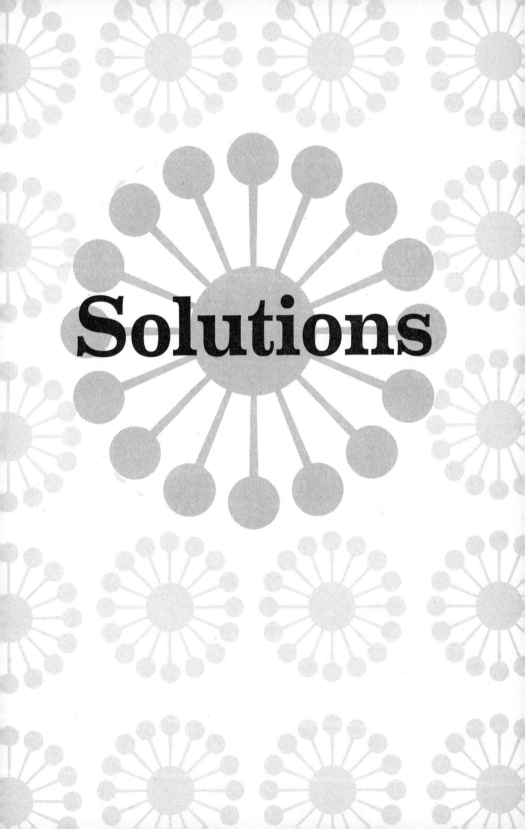

Solutions

1.

4	7	6	1	2	5	9	8	3
5	8	9	4	7	3	6	2	1
1	3	2	8	9	6	7	4	5
8	5	7	3	6	1	2	9	4
9	1	4	5	8	2	3	7	6
6	2	3	9	4	7	5	1	8
2	6	1	7	3	8	4	5	9
3	4	8	2	5	9	1	6	7
7	9	5	6	1	4	8	3	2

3.

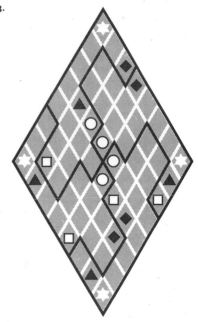

2. Switzerland.

Z	E	D	N
W	T	R	A
I	S	L	P

4. Tide, Idea, Deer, Ears.

5. E.

11	**+**	3	**+**	7	**=**	21

7.

A	B	K	A	Y	N	E	H
R	E	G	I	T		P	A
L	A		N	B	O	A	M
I	R	A	T	U		M	S
O	H	E	K		T	O	T
N	S	N	G	A		L	E
P	I	G	O	D	E	E	R
M	F	G	A	M	A	L	L
E	S	O	O	M		B	

6.

8.

3	8	5	2	1	6	7	4	9
1	4	6	3	7	9	2	8	5
2	7	9	4	8	5	3	1	6
8	3	1	7	6	2	5	9	4
4	6	2	9	5	3	1	7	8
9	5	7	8	4	1	6	2	3
7	1	3	5	9	4	8	6	2
6	2	4	1	3	8	9	5	7
5	9	8	6	2	7	4	3	1

9. The letter 'e'.

> **I live at the beginning of eternity;**
>
> **At the end of time and space;**
>
> **I am the beginning of every end,**
>
> **And the end of every place.**
>
> **Who am I ?**

11. Shell does not belong to the group. The linked words are:

Beast
Decor
Heron
Human
Pilaf
Round

The first and last letter position in the alphabet totals 22.

10. A. 24. Opposite numbers are divided or added to give 24.

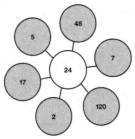

B. 3. Opposite numbers are multiplied or divided by 3.

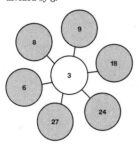

12. Abbreviation. The missing letters are, reading from top to bottom, V, B, N.

E	V	I
R	B	A
A	B	T
N	O	I

13. How many months have 30 days?

11. All except for February, which has either 28 or 29 days.

15. 157 bricks.

□	□	□	□	□	□	□	□	□	□	□	□	□	□	□
	□	□	1	2	3	4	□	□	□	□	□	□	□	□	□
	□	5	6	7	8	9	10	11	12	13	14	□	□	□
	□	15	16	17	18	19	20	21	22	23	24	25	□
	□	26	27	28	29	30	31	32	33	34	35	36	37	□
	□	38	39	40	41	□	□	□	□	□	□	□
	□	□	□	42	43	44	□	□	45	□	□	□	□	□
	□	□	46	47	48	□	□	49	50	□	□	□	□
	□	□	51	52	53	54	55	56	57	58	59	□	□	□
60	61	62	63	64	65	66	67	68	69	70	□	□
	□	71	72	73	74	75	76	77	78	79	80	81	□	□
82	83	84	85	86	87	88	89	90	91	92	93	□
	□	□	94	95	96	97	98	99	100	101	102	103	104	□
	□	□	105	106	107	108	109	110	111	112	113	114	□
	□	□	□	115	□	□	□	□	116	□	□	□	□
	□	□	117	□	118	□	119	120	121	□	122	123	124
	□	125	126	□	□	□	□	□	127	□	□	128	□	□
129	130	□	□	131	□	□	□	132	□	133	134	□
	□	135	136	□	137	138	□	□	139	□	□	140	141	□
	□	□	142	143	144	□	□	145	146	147	148	149
	□	□	□	150	151	152	153	□	□	154	155	156	157	□
	□	□	□	□	□	□	□	□	□	□	□	□	□

14.

2	7	3	9	4	5	8	1	6
8	6	4	1	3	7	5	9	2
1	5	9	2	8	6	7	3	4
6	2	5	3	1	9	4	8	7
3	1	8	7	2	4	6	5	9
9	4	7	6	5	8	3	2	1
5	8	2	4	7	1	9	6	3
7	3	6	5	9	2	1	4	8
4	9	1	8	6	3	2	7	5

16. Kindness

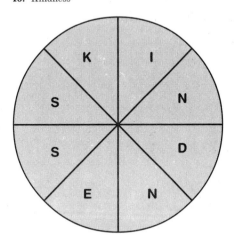

17. F.

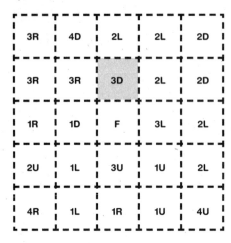

19. They will move apart.

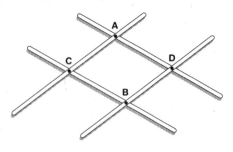

18. E. There are four triangles constantly moving clockwise around the arms and visiting points in sequence.

20.

8	7	4	6	5	9	2	3	1
5	3	2	1	8	7	9	6	4
6	1	9	4	2	3	5	8	7
3	5	7	2	1	6	8	4	9
9	2	1	3	4	8	7	5	6
4	6	8	7	9	5	3	1	2
2	4	3	5	7	1	6	9	8
7	9	6	8	3	4	1	2	5
1	8	5	9	6	2	4	7	3

21. C.

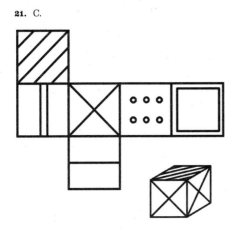

23.

SEEDS
SLEDS
SLEWS
SLOWS
GLOWS
GROWS
GROSS
GRASS

22. 3D in column 1 on row 2.

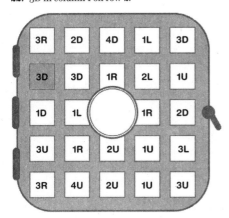

24. B. The alphabetical value of each letter is placed next to it.

G	7
M	13
U	21
J	10
W	23

25. E, G, G. These represent the number 577, which is added to the sum of the previous top and middle line, to get the bottom line.

2	2	9	2
4	3	0	9	E	G	G
7	1	7	8

27. B (Square).

The others are three-dimensional; a square is two-dimensional.

26. D and E. These are rotated mirror images of the other three.

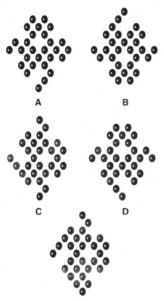

A   B

C   D

E

28. E is the next logical step.

29.

2	7	6	3	5	9	4	8	1
9	5	1	2	4	8	6	7	3
8	3	4	1	7	6	9	2	5
1	9	2	7	6	4	3	5	8
7	8	5	9	3	2	1	4	6
4	6	3	5	8	1	2	9	7
6	2	9	8	1	5	7	3	4
5	4	7	6	9	3	8	1	2
3	1	8	4	2	7	5	6	9

31. E. Opposite segments are mirror images except that black and white shading is reversed.

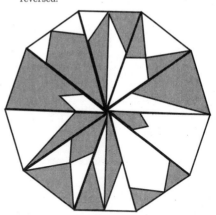

30. C. The number of right angles increases by one each time.

32. Crimson.

STAR	C	ANTS
PLAY	R	BLOW
SACK	I	WANE
ACID	M	SHUT
TEAR	S	ARKS
RIPE	O	VALE
GOAT	N	IONS

33. The eight crossroads are marked.

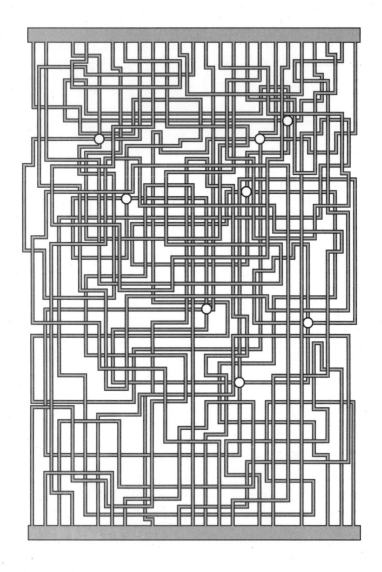

34.

Boys

1	2	3	4	5

Colin	Eddy	Alan	Bill	David

Hilary	Fiona	Indira	Jane	Grace

10	9	8	7	6

Girls

36. C (Open).

35. A. DRK. The others are all colours, but DRK is dark.

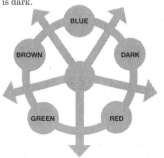

B. BDMNTN. The others are all sports which use a ball. Badminton uses a shuttlecock.

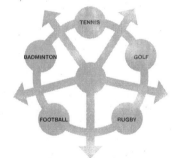

37.

6	3	5	**4**	1	8	**7**	**9**	2
1	8	9	2	**5**	**7**	3	4	**6**
4	**2**	7	3	9	6	5	8	**1**
9	6	8	7	**2**	1	4	**3**	5
2	5	**4**	8	6	**3**	9	**1**	7
7	1	3	**9**	4	5	6	2	**8**
8	7	2	6	**3**	4	1	**5**	9
5	**4**	**6**	**1**	8	9	**2**	7	**3**
3	**9**	1	5	7	2	8	6	4

309

38. Follow this route.

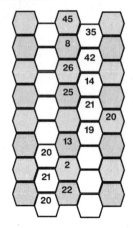

40. 17.

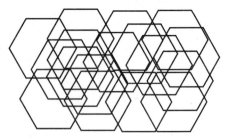

39. E.

41.

30	39	48	1	10	19	28
38	47	7	9	18	27	29
46	6	8	17	26	35	37
5	14	16	25	34	36	45
13	15	24	33	42	44	4
21	23	32	41	43	3	12
22	31	40	49	2	11	20

42. Birmingham.

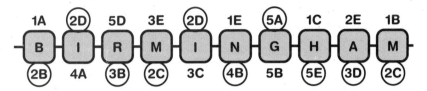

43.

3	9	7	5	1	4	2	8	6
4	1	2	8	6	9	7	5	3
5	8	6	7	3	2	9	1	4
1	6	4	2	7	8	5	3	9
9	3	5	6	4	1	8	7	2
7	2	8	3	9	5	4	6	1
2	5	1	4	8	6	3	9	7
8	7	9	1	2	3	6	4	5
6	4	3	9	5	7	1	2	8

44. Lid, Valid, Quality, and Will.

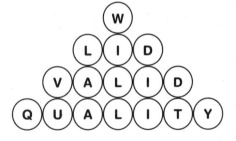

45. C.

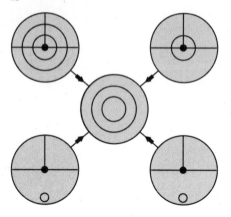

47. The first boy had 16 five-cent coins; the second had 11 ten-cent coins; and the third had 7 fifty-cent coins.

46. There are five odd numbers which follow an even one, so 5 x 5 = 25.

48. A.

49.

Yugoslavia

Australia

Scotland

Russia

Honduras

South Africa

Germany

Barbados

51. D. When completed the box reads the same both down and across

3	2	3	3	2
2	2	3	2	2
3	3	2	3	2
3	2	3	2	2
2	2	2	2	3

50.

8	7	4	6	5	2	9	1	3
5	9	3	1	7	8	2	4	6
6	2	1	4	9	3	7	8	5
9	3	8	2	4	1	5	6	7
7	1	6	8	3	5	4	2	9
2	4	5	9	6	7	8	3	1
1	6	7	5	8	4	3	9	2
3	8	9	7	2	6	1	5	4
4	5	2	3	1	9	6	7	8

52. They drowned when their ship crashed into the rocks. Marianne was a lighthouse keeper!

53. 9 minutes and 9 seconds after 1.

55. 48. Add together the bottom two numbers, multiply the total by the top and place the answer in the middle.

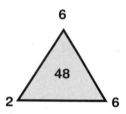

54. The probability that it will be fine on Sunday is found by working out the total number of combinations of weather changes for the next three days. They are:

Fine, fine, fine

Wet, fine, fine

Fine, wet, fine

Wet, wet, fine.

Take the probability for each combination and add them together:

3/4 x 3/4 x 3/4 + 1/4 x 1/3 x 3/4 +3/4 x 1/4 x 1/3 + 1/4 x 2/3 x 1/3, which equals 347/576 - so I think I'll risk walking on Sunday.

56. B. Utter. Each word starts with the second letter of the previous one.

57. If number eight did not require repairing the supervisor should have said that five out of the first seven needed repairing.

59.

6	4	9	5	2	3	1	7	8
3	7	1	6	8	4	5	2	9
5	2	8	1	9	7	6	3	4
7	3	2	8	1	5	9	4	6
4	8	6	2	7	9	3	5	1
1	9	5	3	4	6	7	8	2
8	6	3	4	5	1	2	9	7
2	5	7	9	6	8	4	1	3
9	1	4	7	3	2	8	6	5

58.

1	3	6	9	7	4	8	5	2
9	8	4	2	1	5	3	7	6
7	2	5	8	6	3	4	9	1
5	6	3	4	2	8	7	1	9
8	1	9	6	5	7	2	3	4
2	4	7	1	3	9	6	8	5
3	9	1	7	4	6	5	2	8
4	7	2	5	8	1	9	6	3
6	5	8	3	9	2	1	4	7

60.

8	2	3	6	4	7	5	9	1
1	3	8	7	2	5	9	4	6
4	6	7	1	9	3	8	2	5
9	4	5	8	7	6	3	1	2
7	5	6	9	1	4	2	3	8
6	8	1	2	5	9	4	7	3
2	7	9	3	8	1	6	5	4
3	1	4	5	6	2	7	8	9
5	9	2	4	3	8	1	6	7

61.

5	6	7	8	3	2	9	1	4
3	7	5	6	4	8	2	9	1
2	4	1	3	8	5	7	6	9
4	1	6	2	5	9	8	3	7
9	8	4	1	2	7	3	5	6
8	3	9	7	1	4	6	2	5
6	5	8	9	7	3	1	4	2
7	9	2	5	6	1	4	8	3
1	2	3	4	9	6	5	7	8

63.

4	5	6	8	3	9	7	2	1
8	1	9	7	5	2	6	3	4
2	3	7	4	1	6	5	8	9
7	4	5	1	6	8	2	9	3
3	2	1	9	7	5	8	4	6
6	9	8	3	2	4	1	5	7
9	6	4	2	8	1	3	7	5
1	8	3	5	4	7	9	6	2
5	7	2	6	9	3	4	1	8

62.

6	4	9	2	1	5	7	3	8
7	2	8	3	6	4	1	9	5
5	1	3	7	8	9	4	2	6
9	8	5	6	2	7	3	1	4
1	6	4	9	5	3	8	7	2
2	3	7	1	4	8	6	5	9
8	5	2	4	3	1	9	6	7
4	9	1	5	7	6	2	8	3
3	7	6	8	9	2	5	4	1

64.

Top-left grid:

9	7	8	6	5	1	2	3	4
5	4	2	9	3	8	7	1	6
6	3	1	7	2	4	8	9	5
8	1	6	3	9	7	4	5	2
4	5	9	8	1	2	6	7	3
3	2	7	5	4	6	1	8	9
1	6	3	2	8	5	9	4	7
7	9	4	1	6	3	5	2	8
2	8	5	4	7	9	3	6	1

Top-right grid:

5	3	8	7	9	4	2	1	6
2	9	7	1	5	6	4	3	8
6	4	1	3	2	8	5	9	7
1	8	2	9	7	3	6	4	5
7	6	3	5	4	1	9	8	2
9	5	4	8	6	2	1	7	3
8	3	2	5	4	8	9	7	6
4	1	6	2	3	7	8	5	9
2	8	7	9	6	1	5	3	2

Central connecting block:

7	3	6	4	8	5	1	9	2
8	9	5	3	2	1	7	6	4
2	1	4	9	7	6	5	8	3

Bottom-left grid:

3	7	6	8	9	1	4	5	2
2	5	1	4	3	7	6	8	9
4	9	8	6	2	5	1	7	3
7	6	3	9	5	4	2	1	8
9	1	2	3	8	6	7	4	5
8	4	5	1	7	2	3	9	6
1	2	9	7	6	8	5	3	4
5	3	7	2	4	9	8	6	1
6	8	4	5	1	3	9	2	7

Bottom-right grid:

9	3	1	7	4	6	2	5	8
2	5	7	3	9	8	4	6	1
6	4	8	1	5	2	3	7	9
4	9	6	5	8	1	7	2	3
1	7	5	2	3	9	6	8	4
8	2	3	6	7	4	1	9	5
5	6	4	8	2	3	9	1	7
7	1	9	4	6	5	8	3	2
3	8	2	9	1	7	5	4	6

65. 17 rattlesnakes can be collected if you follow this route:

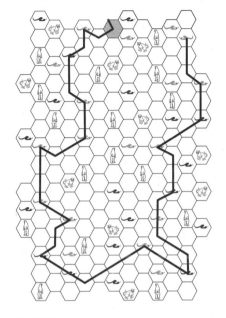

67. 24 ways. There are six alternatives with each suit at the top left.

66. F. (8)

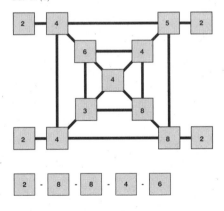

68.

9	1	4	6	3
1	2	5	3	1
4	5	8	0	2
6	3	0	9	6
3	1	2	6	7

69. 25 ways.

71. B.

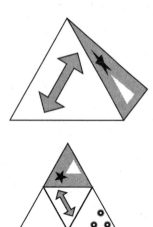

70. A. There are six triangles, each with their base on one of the sides of the hexagon. Each triangle increases in height by a quarter of the width of the hexagon at each stage. So, showing one triangle only:

72. 2U on row 4 in column 4.

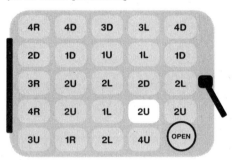

73.

6	3	2	4	9	5	7	1	8
8	7	4	3	2	1	5	6	9
9	5	1	7	6	8	2	3	4
7	2	3	9	5	6	8	4	1
4	8	6	1	3	2	9	7	5
5	1	9	8	4	7	6	2	3
2	6	8	5	1	3	4	9	7
3	9	7	6	8	4	1	5	2
1	4	5	2	7	9	3	8	6

75. Hockey, Karate and Tennis.

74 A and J. The loops have been distorted with respect to the others.

76. Gnomon (a pointer on a sundial).

A   **J**

319

77. Caffeine.

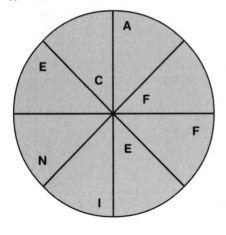

78. C. Each double section totals 10.

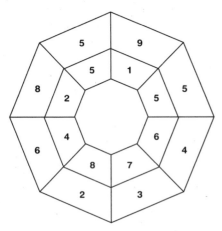

79. 13. The four values are 2, 3, 4 and 5 and the first line read 2 + 4 - 5 = 1.

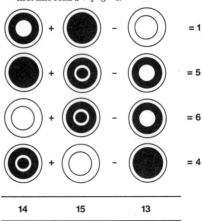

80. Alf Muggins. If it was Jack Vicious, the statements of Alf Muggins and Jim Pouncer would be true. If it was Sid Shifty, the statements of Jack Vicious, Alf Muggins and Jim Pouncer would be true. If it was Jim Pouncer, the statements of Sid Shifty and Alf Muggins would be true. Therefore it is Alf Muggins, and only the statement of Jim Pouncer is true.

81.

6	7	4	8	3	9	2	5	1
2	5	1	6	7	4	8	3	9
9	3	8	5	2	1	4	6	7
8	9	3	1	4	6	7	2	5
1	2	7	3	9	5	6	8	4
4	6	5	7	8	2	1	9	3
5	4	9	2	6	7	3	1	8
3	1	2	4	5	8	9	7	6
7	8	6	9	1	3	5	4	2

83. Den.

RED		OUNCE
BID	DEN	TIN
HID		TIL

REDDEN
BIDDEN
HIDDEN
DENOUNCE
DENTIN
DENTIL

82.

2	5	4	1	9	6	3	8	7
8	6	9	3	7	2	1	5	4
7	1	3	8	5	4	9	2	6
4	7	8	6	1	5	2	9	3
3	9	5	2	4	7	8	6	1
6	2	1	9	3	8	4	7	5
1	8	2	7	6	3	5	4	9
5	3	6	4	2	9	7	1	8
9	4	7	5	8	1	6	3	2

84.

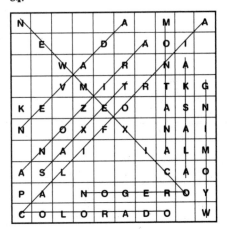

85. Manor House.

Name	Occupation	Pastime	Rest day
Smith	Butler	Squash	Friday
Jones	Gardener	Golf	Tuesday
Wood	Chauffeur	Fishing	Wednesday
Clark	Janitor	Chess	Thursday
James	Cook	Bridge	Monday

86. A. The alphabetical value of each letter is placed next to it.

C	3	14	N
Y	25	12	L
F	6	19	S
U	21	16	P
O	15	4	D

1. Plant belongs to the group. The linked words are:

Burnt
Count
Event
Flint
Giant.

All words end in NT.

2. SCARAB

3. 2519 prisoners.
2519 divided by 3 = 839 tables with 2 over
2519 divided by 5 = 503 tables with 4 over
2519 divided by 7 = 359 with 6 over
2519 divided by 9 = 279 with 8 over
2519 divided by 11 = 229 exactly.

4.

3	8	5	2	1	6	7	4	9
1	4	6	3	7	9	2	8	5
2	7	9	4	8	5	3	1	6
8	3	1	7	6	2	5	9	4
4	6	2	9	5	3	1	7	8
9	5	7	8	4	1	6	2	3
7	1	3	5	9	4	8	6	2
6	2	4	1	3	8	9	5	7
5	9	8	6	2	7	4	3	1

5. 8.

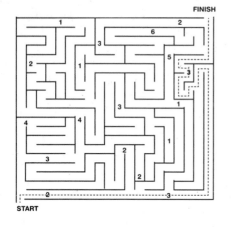

7. Brides and Debris.

AFTER THE DOUBLE WEDDING,
THE TWO <u>BRIDES</u> WALKED
THROUGH THE HALL, WHICH
WAS LITTERED WITH THE
<u>DEBRIS</u> FROM THE PARTY
HELD THE PREVIOUS NIGHT.

6. E (8).

8. C.

9.

2	5	6	9	1	3	8	7	4
1	8	7	2	4	6	3	9	5
9	3	4	7	5	8	1	6	2
4	1	3	5	8	9	6	2	7
7	2	8	4	6	1	9	5	3
5	6	9	3	2	7	4	1	8
6	9	5	8	3	2	7	4	1
3	7	2	1	9	4	5	8	6
8	4	1	6	7	5	2	3	9

11. "If you can't stand the heat keep out of the kitchen." President Harry Truman.

10.

CHOP

SHOP

SHOE

SLOE

FLOE

FLEE

FREE

TREE

12. On the corner of road 5, street 4. Draw a line down the person who is in the middle on the roads axis. Then draw a line across the person who is in the middle of the streets axis.

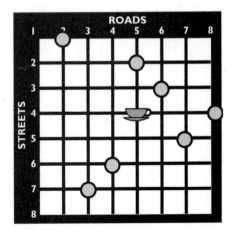

13. B.

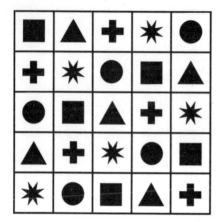

15.

3	7	8	2	4	1	6	5	9
2	5	4	9	8	6	7	1	3
6	1	9	5	3	7	4	2	8
1	9	3	6	7	2	5	8	4
5	4	7	8	9	3	2	6	1
8	2	6	4	1	5	9	3	7
9	6	1	7	2	8	3	4	5
7	3	2	1	5	4	8	9	6
4	8	5	3	6	9	1	7	2

14. B. Each object in the bottom row is a right-hand mirror-image of the shape above so, in this case, the image will be the same as the object.

16. Crumpet.

17. Anastasia tells a lie when she says that the number is below 500. The only square and cube between 99 and 999 whose first and last digit is 5, 7 or 9 is 729.

19.

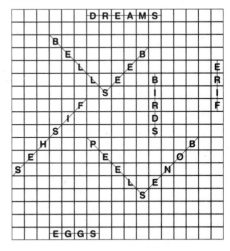

18.

2	1	6	5	3	8	4	9	7
4	3	9	6	7	1	5	8	2
7	5	8	9	4	2	3	6	1
6	7	3	1	5	9	8	2	4
8	4	5	3	2	6	1	7	9
9	2	1	4	8	7	6	5	3
5	8	2	7	1	3	9	4	6
1	9	4	2	6	5	7	3	8
3	6	7	8	9	4	2	1	5

20. A.

B.

bells - campanology, fishes - ichtyology,
bees - apiology, sleep - hypnology,
birds - ornithology, bones - osteology,
dreams - oneirology, eggs - oology, fire - pyrology

21.

```
T O P P O T A T T O T P O P O
O A A T O P A T O T A O P O T
P A P O T T P O T A T T O O A
T A P T O T O T O P O O A T T
O T O P A O T P T P T P O A
O P A T O P A A O T A T A P
A P O A P T P T P T A T P T
T P A P A P T O P T T O T A
O O O A T T A A O O P T A A T
T T O A O T T O P O T A P O
O A T P T P T P A O T O T A P
P O O T A A P A T T O A A P O
P T A T T T T P O P O T T T T
O T A O O P T O P A T P O O O
O P P O T A T T A P A T P E P
```

22.

Found words: HEMINGWAY, DICKENS, AUSTEN, ORWELL

23.

Male	M1	M3	M5	M7	M9
Female	F8	F6	F4	F2	F10
Vehicle	Warp distorter	Galaxy freighter	Space oscillator	Astro-carrier	Nebula accelerator
Speech	Time travel	Nuclear fission	Astral transporting	Anti-gravity	Mind reading
Feature	12 fingers	3 eyes	3 legs	Webbed feet	4 arms

24.

7	1	6	3	4	2	9	5	8
9	5	4	8	7	6	3	1	2
3	2	8	1	5	9	7	6	4
2	4	9	7	1	8	6	3	5
6	7	5	2	3	4	8	9	1
8	3	1	6	9	5	2	4	7
5	6	7	9	8	1	4	2	3
4	9	3	5	2	7	1	8	6
1	8	2	4	6	3	5	7	9

26. 15:03 (or 03.15 (pm) if the watch has the capacity to switch to 12-hour mode).

25. A. Tango, Polka, Rumba, Samba.

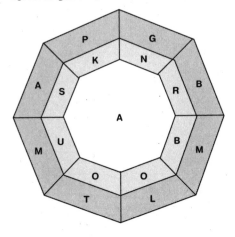

27. Step.

Doorstep
Footstep
Overstep
Sidestep
Quickstep
Instep

28. E.

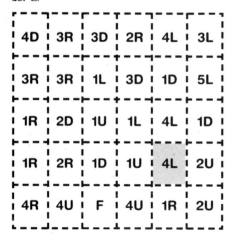

30. Spencer prunes six more trees than Don. If there are x number of trees on both sides, we know that Don prunes three trees on the right-hand side, before pruning x-6 trees on his side, resulting in x-3 trees pruned. Spencer must therefore prune x+3 trees, meaning he has pruned 6 more trees.

29. A. Looking both across and down, the contents of the third square are formed by merging the contents of the two previous squares as follows:

One white or black circle remains;
Two black circles become white;
Two white circles become black.

31.

4	3	6	7	5	8	1	2	9
5	9	2	3	6	1	8	7	4
7	8	1	9	2	4	6	3	5
6	1	9	4	7	2	5	8	3
2	5	8	1	9	3	4	6	7
3	7	4	5	8	6	9	1	2
8	4	7	6	3	9	2	5	1
1	2	5	8	4	7	3	9	6
9	6	3	2	1	5	7	4	8

32. Daniel, Exodus, Isaiah and Joshua can be found by pairing alternate segments.

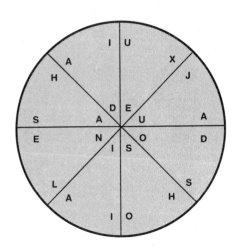

34. A.

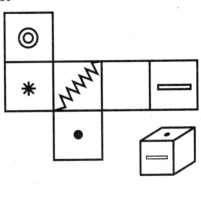

33. Harmonium, Accordion, Piano, and Tuba.

D	I	I	O	N	O	U
T						A
N		C	C	H		N
O		A		O		I
M				A		M
U	R	B	A	R		P

35.

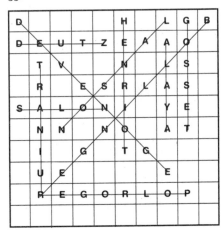

36. Algeria. The words are: teA, niL, foG, tiE, baR, obI, and erA.

38. 2 units. The difference of 18 divided by 9. The units to the right come to 104, to the left they are 86 (both sides have 24x and 24y). 104 – 86 = 18. The blank box is 9 units across so 2 x 9 = 18.

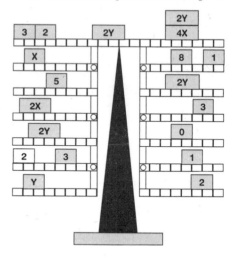

37.

5	3	6	4	7	1	8	2	9
8	4	2	3	9	6	1	7	5
9	7	1	2	5	8	3	6	4
7	6	5	1	3	9	4	8	2
1	2	3	8	4	7	5	9	6
4	8	9	6	2	5	7	3	1
6	9	7	5	1	3	2	4	8
2	1	8	7	6	4	9	5	3
3	5	4	9	8	2	6	1	7

39. B. The minute hand moves forward ten minutes and the hour hand one hour on each clock.

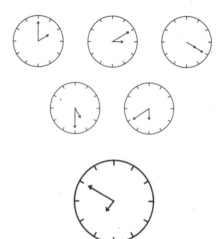

40.

Tree	Elm	Ash	Beech	Lime	Poplar
Person	Bill	Jim	Tony	Sylvester	Desmond
Club	Squash	Golf	Tennis	Bowling	Soccer
Bird	Owl	Blackbird	Crow	Robin	Starling
Year	1970	1971	1972	1973	1974

41. The cartoon characters are: Bambi, Cinderella, Pluto and Yogi.

I 24	R 11	P 16	I 5	O 22
B 1	C 6	G 23	E 10	A 15
E 12	L 17		Y 21	B 4
I 7	A 2	T 19	L 14	D 9
U 18	L 13	N 8	M 3	O 20

42.

6	1	8	2	9	5	3	7	4
4	7	3	6	1	8	9	5	2
2	9	5	3	7	4	8	1	6
5	8	9	4	6	3	7	2	1
1	6	4	8	2	7	5	3	9
3	2	7	9	5	1	6	4	8
8	5	2	7	4	6	1	9	3
9	3	1	5	8	2	4	6	7
7	4	6	1	3	9	2	8	5

1.

1	5	2	4	3	6	9	8	7
6	7	9	8	2	5	3	4	1
8	3	4	9	1	7	6	5	2
4	9	7	3	6	8	2	1	5
2	1	6	5	9	4	7	3	8
5	8	3	2	7	1	4	6	9
7	4	8	6	5	2	1	9	3
3	6	1	7	8	9	5	2	4
9	2	5	1	4	3	8	7	6

3. Carter, Eisenhower, Johnson, Reagan, Roosevelt.

2. 2. If all 49 women wore glasses then 21 men wore glasses too. If 11 of these men were under 20 years of age, only 10 men older than 20 years of age wore glasses. Then 10 – 8 = 2 men is the minimum number.

4. Summer Vacations.

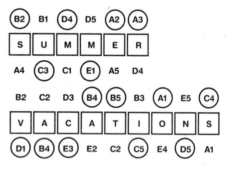

5. B. Looking both across and down, any lines common to the first two tiles disappear in the third tile.

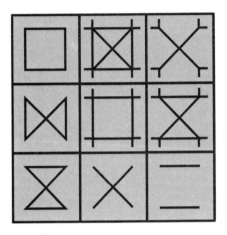

7. Meaningful.

6. C. The sequece repeats every 5 tiles with a different shape.

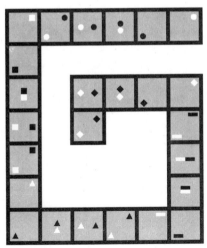

8.

9.

3	5	6	8	7	9	4	2	1
1	8	4	5	2	3	9	7	6
2	9	7	6	4	1	5	3	8
7	1	2	9	5	6	3	8	4
5	6	8	3	1	4	2	9	7
4	3	9	7	8	2	1	6	5
9	7	3	1	6	5	8	4	2
8	2	1	4	3	7	6	5	9
6	4	5	2	9	8	7	1	3

11. Y.

B	R	Y	A	N
A	N	B	R	Y
R	Y	A	N	B
N	B	R	Y	A
Y	A	N	B	R

10. C.

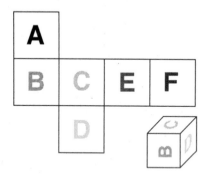

12.

9	7	5	2	3	1	4	6	8
2	6	1	8	5	4	3	7	9
4	8	3	6	7	9	2	5	1
6	1	8	4	9	5	7	3	2
3	4	2	7	8	6	1	9	5
7	5	9	3	1	2	6	8	4
1	3	7	5	4	8	9	2	6
5	9	6	1	2	7	8	4	3
8	2	4	9	6	3	5	1	7

13.

5	1	9	9	★	1	2	6	★	2	8	0	1
3	★	★	9	3	2	★	4	2	1	★	★	1
6	2	8	9	★	7	3	8	★	1	3	6	6
2	★	2	8	0	3	★	4	1	9	0	★	3
9	★	2	★	★	5	★	3	★	★	0	★	5
3	4	8	5	★	★	★	★	★	4	2	2	7
★	9	★	9	1	2	4	9	1	4	★	0	★
1	2	3	3	4	★	1	★	5	3	8	0	2
★	6	★	6	★	1	4	9	★	6	★	9	★
5	6	1	8	2	★	3	★	1	2	3	0	4
★	0	★	0	6	9	3	8	7	8	★	0	★
9	★	5	★	1	★	8	★	1	★	6	★	5
8	6	4	★	1	2	3	4	5	★	1	1	8
1	★	2	3	4	5	★	2	1	3	3	★	6
9	7	8	3	★	★	★	★	★	9	2	7	7
2	★	2	★	★	2	★	1	★	★	1	★	1
1	★	9	1	3	4	★	5	6	6	0	★	3
6	3	2	1	★	9	8	7	★	3	4	8	2
0	★	★	7	6	9	★	8	2	3	★	★	2
3	4	5	8	★	1	9	7	★	4	6	5	6

14. C (12).

50 35 0 0
50 20 15 0
45 40 0 0
45 25 15 0
45 20 20 0
40 25 20 0
40 15 15 15
35 25 25 0
35 20 15 15
35 35 15 0
25 25 20 15
25 20 20 20

16.

A. A6, C5, G6.

B. D2.

C. 12.

D. 117, occurs 3 times.

E. 91, G1.

F. E4.

G. None.

H. None.

15. The dalmations are called Andy (owned by Bill) and Donald (owned by Colin). Bill also owns a corgi named Donald, and Colin owns a labrador named Bill. Andy owns a corgi named Bill and a labrador named Colin, and Donald owns a labrador named Andy and a corgi named Colin.

17.

5	4	9	8	3	2	6	1	7
3	6	1	4	7	9	2	5	8
7	2	8	6	1	5	3	9	4
6	3	5	1	2	7	8	4	9
8	9	7	5	6	4	1	2	3
4	1	2	9	8	3	5	7	6
9	5	3	2	4	8	7	6	1
2	8	6	7	9	1	4	3	5
1	7	4	3	5	6	9	8	2

18.

i) Roberto Baggio

ii) Dennis Bergkamp

iii) Kevin Keegan

iv) Eric Cantona

v) Jurgen Klinsmann

20. D. The three squares form four triangles.

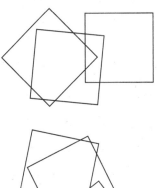

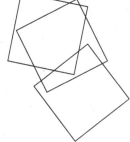

19. Woodbine

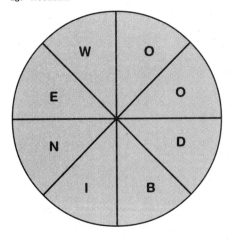

21. 12. The number of letters between the alphanumeric position of the first and last letters of each name.

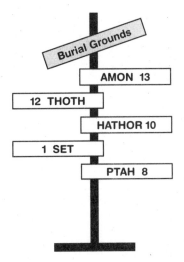

22.

2	4	3	9	8	7	1	6	5
8	1	7	5	6	3	9	4	2
6	5	9	4	1	2	8	3	7
4	3	5	2	7	9	6	1	8
1	2	8	6	3	5	7	9	4
7	9	6	1	4	8	5	2	3
5	6	4	8	2	1	3	7	9
9	7	1	3	5	4	2	8	6
3	8	2	7	9	6	4	5	1

24.

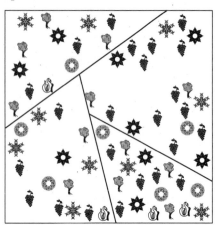

23. B. The sequence always adds two double-curved lines onto the end of the previous pattern, at the end of the last new point added.

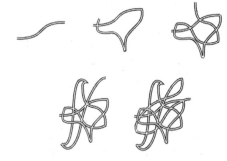

25. C. The same seven objects are repeated continuously in each line, regardless of tone.

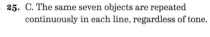
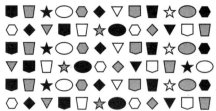

26.

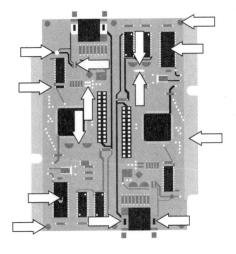

28. Separated and decorator

27. Rococo, Rubato, Sonata, Timbre

The first letter of two of the routes is the same and the last letter of two of the routes is the same.

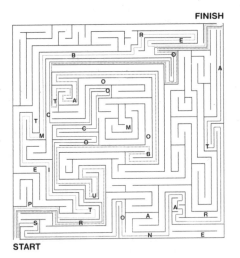

29. 1. If you don't believe this, hold the book up to a mirror. You will see that with the inclusion of the above, the numbers 2, 3, 4, 5 appear in sequence.

30. Rainbow.

GLOW	R	BEAT
CONE	A	DOME
HAVE	I	MACE
SHOW	N	ITCH
IRIS	B	ILEX
READ	O	LIVE
STAG	W	SLAB

32.

6	9	3	7	1	8	4	2	5
5	7	4	6	2	3	9	8	1
8	1	2	9	5	4	3	6	7
3	6	9	8	7	1	2	5	4
4	2	8	3	6	5	1	7	9
1	5	7	2	4	9	8	3	6
9	3	5	1	8	7	6	4	2
2	4	1	5	3	6	7	9	8
7	8	6	4	9	2	5	1	3

31.

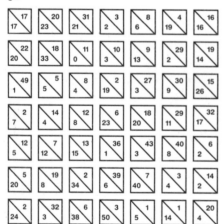

33. Mow, Jewel, Blanket and Down.

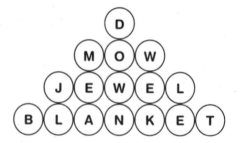

34. Lines are through those words that run together, for clarity.

36. Chicago.

35. E. The alphabetical positions of the letters are found and the smaller is taken from the larger.

A	1	B
D	7	K
Q	2	O
R	2	T
Z	23	C

37. So that:

1. No two consecutive numbers appear in any horizontal, vertical or diagonal line;

2. No two consecutive numbers appear in adjacent squares.

Note also the positions of 1 and 2 could be swapped.

38. E. routine : abnormal. They are antonyms as are doubt and conviction

40.

6	2	1	3	8	5	4	7	9
9	8	4	2	1	7	6	5	3
5	7	3	6	9	4	2	8	1
2	5	8	7	4	9	1	3	6
3	1	6	5	2	8	9	4	7
7	4	9	1	6	3	5	2	8
8	9	5	4	7	1	3	6	2
1	3	2	8	5	6	7	9	4
4	6	7	9	3	2	8	1	5

39.

A. 3.87. 116 passes for 30 students.

B. 3.32. 83 passes for 25 students.

C. 58.

41. WEDNESDAY

42.

Anne studies algebra, history, French and Japanese.

Bess studies physics, English, History and Japanese.

Candice studies algebra, physics, English and French.

44. 20. Each vowel is worth 4 and each consonant 2. The totals of the vowels and consonants are added.

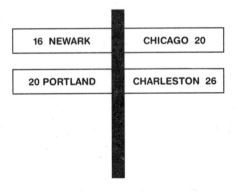

43.

45.

7	3	1	2	9	4	5	8	6
6	9	5	3	1	8	4	7	2
4	8	2	5	6	7	9	3	1
3	4	6	8	2	9	1	5	7
5	7	9	1	4	6	3	2	8
2	1	8	7	5	3	6	4	9
9	6	7	4	8	5	2	1	3
8	2	4	6	3	1	7	9	5
1	5	3	9	7	2	8	6	4

46. D.

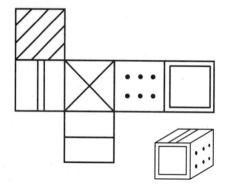

47. J is option 4; N is option 6. The black segments move from top to bottom and right to left in sequence, then rise in the same way. However, when an arrangement has occurred previously it is omitted from the sequence.

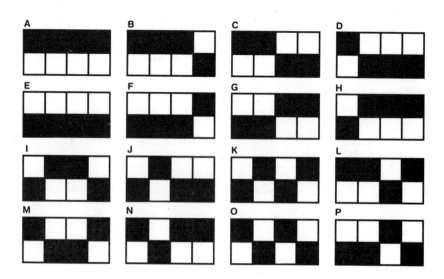

1.

Name	Class	Subject	Sport
Alice	6	Algebra	Squash
Betty	2	Biology	Running
Clara	4	History	Swimming
Doris	3	Geography	Tennis
Elizabeth	5	Chemistry	Basketball

2.

7	6	4	9	3	2	1	8	5
8	5	1	4	7	6	2	3	9
3	2	9	8	5	1	7	6	4
6	7	5	1	9	3	4	2	8
9	1	2	6	8	4	3	5	7
4	8	3	7	2	5	9	1	6
1	9	7	2	6	8	5	4	3
5	4	6	3	1	7	8	9	2
2	3	8	5	4	9	6	7	1

3. O. The middle letter of each name is in the middle of the box. Fonda, Hanks, Wayne and Stone.

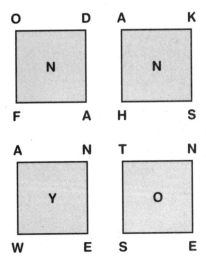

4.

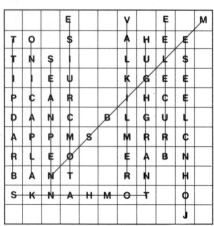

6. MIDGE
EMMET
APHID
LOUSE
DRONE

5. D. MANS GUT (mustang). The others are:

PUMPKIN (MILK PUP)

BLUEBERRY (BURY REBEL)

SATSUMA (USA MAST)

MANDARIN (DAMN RAIN).

7. 25 minutes. As the man leaves home according to his normal schedule it is earlier than 6.30 pm when he picks up his wife. As the total journey saves 10 minutes, that must be the same time it takes the man from the point he picks up his wife to the station and back to the same point. Assuming that it takes an equal five minutes each way he has therefore picked up his wife five minutes before he would normally, which means 6.20pm. So his wife must have walked from 6.00pm to 6.25pm, that is for 25 minutes.

8.

⊕	3	0	⊕	9	8	9	⊕	5	1	6	⊕	7	4	⊕
1	4	8	⊕	4	6	7	⊕	3	9	0	⊕	5	6	3
6	4	4	5	5	3	5	⊕	6	2	8	1	3	0	7
5	⊕	0	⊕	2	⊕	9	5	4	⊕	9	⊕	3	⊕	2
2	7	3	⊕	6	5	9	⊕	7	2	1	⊕	6	9	1
6	4	9	0	9	1	6	⊕	4	3	4	6	5	4	0
3	8	6	⊕	5	7	8	3	9	6	8	⊕	2	9	8
⊕	5	⊕	⊕	⊕	6	⊕	3	⊕	9	⊕	⊕	⊕	7	⊕
3	5	9	⊕	9	4	7	3	4	6	0	⊕	3	0	6
2	7	6	8	2	5	9	⊕	9	7	9	8	2	5	9
0	1	8	⊕	1	3	3	⊕	0	4	2	⊕	6	9	7
4	⊕	7	⊕	9	⊕	4	9	6	⊕	9	⊕	8	⊕	4
6	9	0	6	3	0	8	⊕	7	5	9	0	9	3	6
9	2	9	⊕	6	4	9	⊕	3	2	6	⊕	5	1	9
⊕	8	7	⊕	7	3	5	⊕	6	1	9	⊕	9	3	⊕

9. Winston Churchill

W	I	N	S
T	O	N	C
H	U	R	C
H	I	L	L

11.

1. Player 2.

2. Player 3.

3. Player 6.

4. Player 3.

5. Players 1 and 5.

6. Players 1, 4 and 6.

7. 21.

8. 46.

10.

8	4	7	2	6	9	5	3	1
2	3	9	5	4	1	8	6	7
1	6	5	8	3	7	9	4	2
5	9	1	6	2	3	7	8	4
3	2	8	7	1	4	6	5	9
4	7	6	9	8	5	1	2	3
9	5	4	3	7	6	2	1	8
6	1	2	4	9	8	3	7	5
7	8	3	1	5	2	4	9	6

12.

7	8	6	5	4	9	1	3	2
1	4	2	3	6	7	8	9	5
3	5	9	1	8	2	4	6	7
8	7	5	4	1	3	6	2	9
6	3	1	2	9	5	7	4	8
9	2	4	8	7	6	5	1	3
2	9	8	6	5	1	3	7	4
4	1	3	7	2	8	9	5	6
5	6	7	9	3	4	2	8	1

13. 57. The alphanumeric values of each letter are added together in each word to give the word's total value.

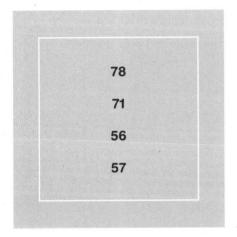

14. E. The two figures merge into one by superimposing one onto the other, except that when two lines appear in the same position they disappear.

15. K. To give Joked, Maker, Taken, and Yokel.

16. C. Give the letters their value in the alphabet and add them to the numbers. The top half of the circle will total 50, as will the bottom half.

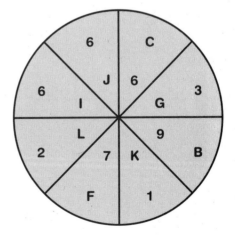

17.

C MR

C MRS

19.

4	6	8	3	7	9	1	2	5
7	1	2	8	4	5	6	9	3
9	3	5	1	6	2	8	4	7
8	9	7	2	1	6	5	3	4
1	2	4	7	5	3	9	6	8
6	5	3	9	8	4	7	1	2
2	7	9	6	3	8	4	5	1
3	4	1	5	9	7	2	8	6
5	8	6	4	2	1	3	7	9

18. The stars are:

Tom Cruise
Mel Gibson
Robert De Niro
Steve Martin
Whoopi Goldberg
Jane Fonda

20. D.

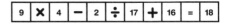

21.

Name	Age	Ride	Food
Sam	14	Dodgems	Hot dog
Joe	11	Big dipper	Fries
Don	12	Whirligig	Candy floss
Len	15	Crocodile	Gum
Ron	13	Mountain	Ice cream

22.

Male	Female	City	Transport
Bob	Mary	Madrid	Bus
Sam	Judith	Paris	Ferry
Alf	Kate	New York	Cruise
Len	Sally	Rome	Plane
Ben	Fiona	Berlin	Train

23.

Name	Fancy Dress	Clothes	Dance
Henry	Dracula	Leggings	Bossa-Nova
Robert	Napoleon	Jack Boots	Charleston
Simon	Dr Jekyll	Fedora	Jitterbug
Peter	Frankenstein	Homburg	Palaid Glide
Morris	Shakespeare	Skull-cap	Barn Dance

24.

Father	Daughter	Father's age	Daughter's age
John	Alison	52	20
Kevin	Diana	53	19
Len	Betty	50	21
Malcolm	Eve	54	18
Nick	Carol	51	17

25. 722m. The path takes up the area of the garden, or 1,444m. It is 2m wide, so it's length is 722m.

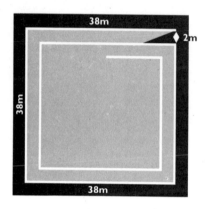

26. Two segments: all the triangles do not need to be the same size.

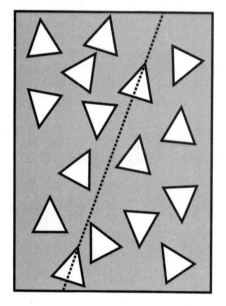

27. Ten.

Tenabale
Tenpin
Tenfold
Tendon
Tenant

28. CASSEROLE, FRICASSEE, MINCEMEAT, SCHNITZEL, SPAGHETTI, HAMBURGER.

C	A	S	S	E	R	O	L	E
F	R	I	C	A	S	S	E	E
M	I	N	C	E	M	E	A	T
S	C	H	N	I	T	Z	E	L
S	P	A	G	H	E	T	T	I
H	A	M	B	U	R	G	E	R

29.

4	2	6	7	5	9	1	8	3
5	3	1	8	6	2	4	7	9
7	9	8	3	4	1	2	5	6
1	8	9	4	3	7	6	2	5
2	5	4	9	1	6	8	3	7
6	7	3	5	2	8	9	4	1
3	6	5	1	8	4	7	9	2
9	4	2	6	7	5	3	1	8
8	1	7	2	9	3	5	6	4

31.

1. Einstein
2. Celsius
3. Newton
4. Copernicus
5. Pascal
6. Darwin

30. 1009315742. The number of white boxes before the shaded box on each line, counting alternately from left and right.

32.

7	8	6	9	2	5	1	4	3
1	3	4	6	8	7	5	9	2
9	5	2	4	1	3	8	7	6
5	6	1	8	4	9	3	2	7
4	9	8	3	7	2	6	5	1
2	7	3	1	5	6	9	8	4
8	1	7	5	6	4	2	3	9
6	4	9	2	3	8	7	1	5
3	2	5	7	9	1	4	6	8

33.

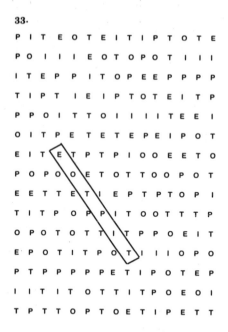

24. N. Monet, Rodin, Munch, Ernst.

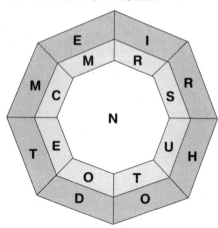

34. C. When completed every row and column sums to 24.

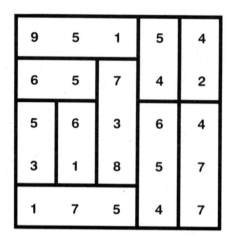

36. A. At each stage the big hand moves anti-clockwise first by 10 minutes, then 20 and, finally, by 30 minutes (option A). At each stage the small hand moves clockwise first by one hour, then two hours and, finally, three hours (option A).

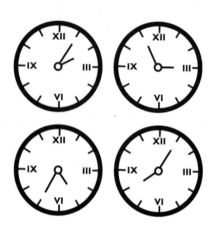

37. F. The alphabetical values of the letters are placed on opposite sides in the middle space.

F	136	M
U	421	D
H	178	Q
O	115	A
X	924	I

39.

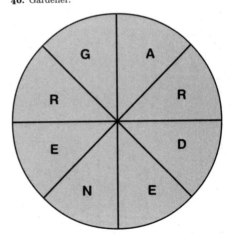

38. Cerise.

40. Gardener.

41.

7	6	4	3	1	2	8	9	5
5	9	1	4	7	8	6	2	3
2	3	8	5	9	6	4	7	1
1	7	3	2	6	4	5	8	9
9	5	6	8	3	7	1	4	2
8	4	2	9	5	1	7	3	6
6	2	7	1	8	9	3	5	4
3	8	9	6	4	5	2	1	7
4	1	5	7	2	3	9	6	8

43.

22	21	13	5	46	38	30
31	23	15	14	6	47	39
40	32	24	16	8	7	48
49	41	33	25	17	9	1
2	43	42	34	26	18	10
11	3	44	36	35	27	19
20	12	4	45	37	29	28

42.

44. Ram.

Rambled
Rampant
Rampage
Ramrods
Rampart
Ramjets

45. No. He disliked places with an i in the name.

46.

7	9	4	3	2	8	5	1	6
5	6	8	4	9	1	3	2	7
1	3	2	7	5	6	8	4	9
4	8	9	2	6	3	7	5	1
2	1	7	5	4	9	6	3	8
3	5	6	1	8	7	2	9	4
8	2	5	6	1	4	9	7	3
9	4	3	8	7	2	1	6	5
6	7	1	9	3	5	4	8	2

1.

3	9	1	8	5	2	4	6	7
6	4	2	7	1	9	3	5	8
7	8	5	6	4	3	2	9	1
4	7	3	5	9	1	6	8	2
5	2	6	4	8	7	9	1	3
9	1	8	3	2	6	7	4	5
1	6	9	2	7	5	8	3	4
8	3	7	1	6	4	5	2	9
2	5	4	9	3	8	1	7	6

2. B (Repartee). Repartee is a synonym for badinage, as taunt is for gibe.

3. 3A (missing central circle).

4. D (beggar).

5. 55

5x5=1
4x4=4
3x3=9
2x2=16
1x1=25

Total = 55

6. E. Fire is extinguised by a fire extinguisher as dirt is removed by a vacuum cleaner.

is to

as DIRT is to

8.

F	A		C	E		T
A	B		O	V		E
C	O	V		E		N
E	V	E		N		T
T	E	N		T		S

7. Ripens and Sniper

IN THE FOREST AS THE

FRUIT RIPENS THE

FURTIVE SNIPER LURKS

IN ANTICIPATION OF HIS

VICTIM.

9.

7	3	1	2	9	4	5	8	6
6	9	5	3	1	8	4	7	2
4	8	2	5	6	7	9	3	1
3	4	6	8	2	9	1	5	7
5	7	9	1	4	6	3	2	8
2	1	8	7	5	3	6	4	9
9	6	7	4	8	5	2	1	3
8	2	4	6	3	1	7	9	5
1	5	3	9	7	2	8	6	4

10.

3	3	8		7	5	5	4	4	0	3		4	4	7
6	5	0		6	9	2		2	6	3		6	6	0
0	3	7	9	3	0	4		9	9	7	4	5	1	5
2		6		2		7	7	8		4		0		7
9	7	4		1	7	1		1	2	2		7	1	1
7	0	6	2	5	0	2		6	5	7	9	8	0	4
6	9	7		4	9	7	1	4	6	7		6	2	7
	7				7		0		7				8	
1	4	7		4	2	5	6	7	0	1		7	5	8
5	2	3	1	9	3	7		6	3	6	8	9	0	6
0	9	6		7	0	6		0	9	2		4	7	2
8		4		8		8	4	7		7		8		1
1	7	5	1	1	7	1		1	5	1	8	1	1	7
7	2	6		1	0	6	2	3	8	7		3	2	8
1	0	1			9			8	4			7	6	
	4			1	6	7			6	9			9	7
5	1	7		9	5	1	2	2	0	9		4	5	0
1	2	9	1	7	6	2		9	5	1	1	1	9	8
7		7		0		1	7	8		2		2		1
2	3	9		7	5	1		9	3	0		9	5	7
6	5	9	6	8	1	7		1	7	6	1	6	7	0
8	2	1		8	3	6	9	5	9	1		1	3	1

11. B. Billy's plot has the greatest perimeter.

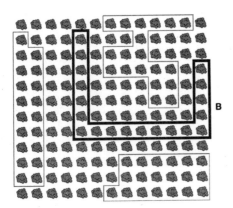

13. F.

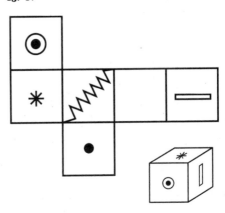

12. B. A anf F are the same, as are C and D, and E and G.

14.

10	1	– 8	39	30	21	12
2	–7	33	31	22	13	11
–6	34	32	23	14	5	3
35	26	24	15	6	4	-5
27	25	16	7	–2	–4	36
19	17	8	–1	–3	37	28
18	9	0	–9	38	29	20

15.

7	5	6	1	3	4	9	8	2
3	8	9	2	7	5	1	6	4
4	1	2	9	6	8	7	3	5
6	9	8	4	5	7	2	1	3
2	4	1	3	9	6	5	7	8
5	3	7	8	1	2	4	9	6
9	6	4	7	2	3	8	5	1
1	2	5	6	8	9	3	4	7
8	7	3	5	4	1	6	2	9

17. A.

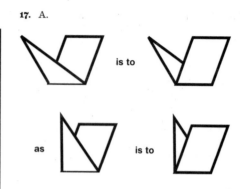

16. 31 kangaroos.

18. D.

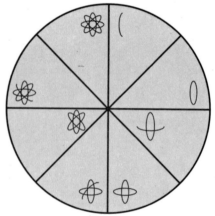

19. C. The square turns 90° clockwise at each stage. Similarly, the shading also moves one segment clockwise at each stage.

21. Had, Blink, Academy and Raid.

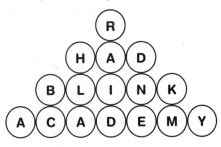

20. D. Different symbols in adjoining circles on the same row are carried into the circle between them in the row above. Similar symbols in the same place are dropped.

22.

7	3	1	2	9	4	5	8	6
6	9	5	3	1	8	4	7	2
4	8	2	5	6	7	9	3	1
3	4	6	8	2	9	1	5	7
5	7	9	1	4	6	3	2	8
2	1	8	7	5	3	6	4	9
9	6	7	4	8	5	2	1	3
8	2	4	6	3	1	7	9	5
1	5	3	9	7	2	8	6	4

22. Jim had moved from his home town years ago. He was watching the floods on the TV news. His wife had never liked the place anyway.

25. Holes or beams of light

23. The old man had given them time. He left each of them the equivalent of their annual salary so that they could have a year to do what they liked.

26. They were grandmother, mother, and daughter. Two were mothers and two were daughters.

27. Because three of them are on my wristwatch.

I have five hands

but you would pass

me in the street

without comment.

Why?

29.

7	10	8	11
4	7	5	8
6	9	7	10
3	6	4	7

28. 8. The sum of each line of three digits comes to 20.

30. 139.

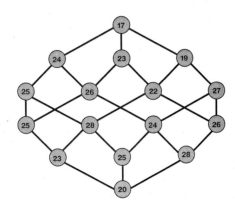

31.

3	8	5	2	1	6	7	4	9
1	4	6	3	7	9	2	8	5
2	7	9	4	8	5	3	1	6
8	3	1	7	6	2	5	9	4
4	6	2	9	5	3	1	7	8
9	5	7	8	4	1	6	2	3
7	1	3	5	9	4	8	6	2
6	2	4	1	3	8	9	5	7
5	9	8	6	2	7	4	3	1

32. Night.

NIGHTtime
NIGHTclub
NIGHTlatch
NIGHTcap
NIGHTdress

33. The helicopter (worth 2).
The symbols have the following values:

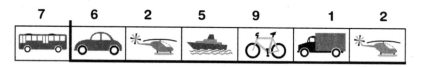

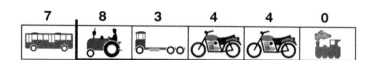

34. Ward. Each word can be prefixed by BACK, making:

BACKgammon
BACKache
BACKtrack,
BACKward.

36. V. To give Civic, Devil (or Lived), Haven, and Lever.

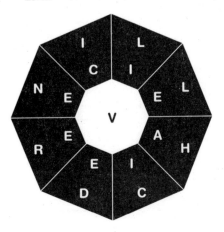

35.

2	9	1	8	4	3	7	5	6
7	5	4	1	9	6	8	2	3
6	3	8	5	2	7	9	1	4
8	1	5	6	7	9	4	3	2
4	7	3	2	8	1	5	6	9
9	2	6	3	5	4	1	7	8
3	6	9	4	1	5	2	8	7
1	4	2	7	3	8	6	9	5
5	8	7	9	6	2	3	4	1

37. D.

38. D.

40. 39 cobras.

39. 24. Start moving from the top left of each hexagon and moving right, opposite numbers are subtracted, then the three resulting numbers are added together to give the central number.

30 - 20 = 10
28 - 21 = 7
14 - 7 = 7
Total = 24

41.

5	7	9	3	2	1	6	4	8
6	8	2	4	5	9	1	7	3
4	1	3	7	8	6	9	2	5
3	4	5	1	7	8	2	6	9
8	2	7	6	9	5	3	1	4
1	9	6	2	3	4	5	8	7
7	3	8	9	1	2	4	5	6
9	6	1	5	4	7	8	3	2
2	5	4	8	6	3	7	9	1

42. Casket. It is a box, the others are jars, normally made of glass.

44. WIDOW belongs to the group associated with Dread, Kiosk, Loyal, Arena, and Comic. Each word begins and ends with the same letter.

43. CORIOLANUS was written by Shakespeare. BARNABY RUDGE, OLIVER TWIST, EDWIN DROOD, were all written by Charles Dickens.

45. Follow the diagram as shown until you reach point B. Then place one foot in C and say, 'As one foot has been in cell C it has undoubtedly been entered. However, when that foot is withdrawn into B I do not enter B for a second time because I never left it.'

CORIOLANUS

BARNABY RUDGE

OLIVER TWIST

EDWIN DROOD

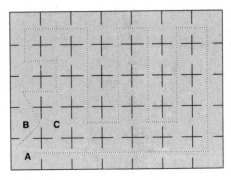

46. A. Reading across rows and down columns, unique elements in the first two are transferred to the third (bottom or right). common elements disappear.

48. C. Others rotate into the same shape.

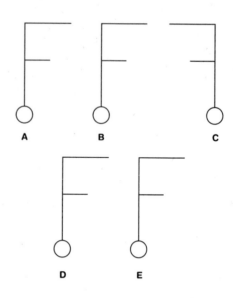

47. B. Reading left to right and up to down, symbols within the first two texagons are repeated, except where they appear in both, then neither are repeated.

49. CENTAVO, GUILDER, PIASTRE, DENARII, MILREID (not an anagram)

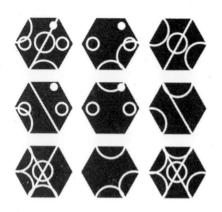

CENTAVO

GUILDER

PIASTRE

DENARII

MILREID

50.

5	1	4	3	8	7	6	2	9
9	2	8	4	5	6	3	1	7
3	7	6	2	1	9	5	4	8
1	6	7	5	2	8	4	9	3
2	3	9	6	7	4	8	5	1
4	8	5	1	9	3	2	7	6
6	4	2	9	3	1	7	8	5
8	5	1	7	6	2	9	3	4
7	9	3	8	4	5	1	6	2

52. B. Reading across columns and down rows of shields, common elements with the same shading in the first two are transferred to the third (bottom or right) and change shading. Unique elements disappear.

51. F.

53. Follow the black route.

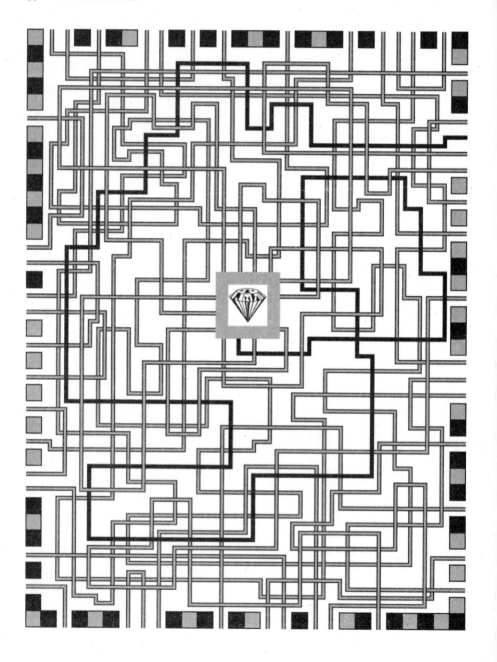

54. Deduction Sequence: 636. Each number describes consecutive square numbers, that is:

$1^2 = 1$ (the first square number is 1)

$2^2 = 4$ (the second square number is 4)

and so on.

The sixth square number is 36, ($6^2 = 36$) or 636.

56.

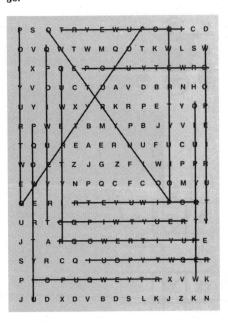

55. He had ordered a bicycle which had arrived in 185 pieces for assembly, which was not stated in the catalogue, so this was his revenge.

57. Hoopoe (a bird).

58.

DROP
PROP
POOP
POOL
POLL
PALL
FALL

60.

9	1	5	4	3	2	7	8	6
6	7	4	8	9	1	5	3	2
8	3	2	6	5	7	9	4	1
4	8	6	2	1	9	3	7	5
3	9	1	7	4	5	6	2	8
2	5	7	3	6	8	4	1	9
7	6	8	5	2	4	1	9	3
5	4	9	1	8	3	2	6	7
1	2	3	9	7	6	8	5	4

59. B (W).

61.

18	6	4	30	47	29
45	30	6	18	17	2
1	21	1	42	23	5
3	28	7	17	1	6
44	4	32	43	30	40

6	2	3	4	4	3
3	5	5	2	6	2
5	3	1	3	5	0
2	4	5	3	0	5
3	3	4	6	6	5

62. Intercontinental

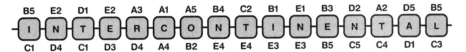

B5	E2	D1	E2	A3	A1	A5	B4	C2	B1	E1	B3	D2	A2	D5	B5
I	N	T	E	R	C	O	N	T	I	N	E	N	T	A	L
C1	D4	C1	D3	D4	A4	B2	E4	E4	E3	E3	B5	C5	C4	D1	C3

63.

64. Calypso.

THIN	C	RAGE
SKIN	A	FIRS
WIFE	L	BUMP
SOUR	Y	TANK
DARK	P	MOST
CHIP	S	WEAR
WILY	O	BATH

65. 47 coins contained in 10 bags all deposited on outside plots, thus 4, 5 and 6 in the first row, 5 in the second, 4 in the third, 3 in the fourth, 5 in the fifth, and 5, 6, 4 in the bottom row.

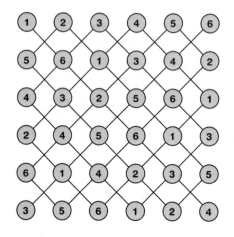

67.

Assume 2 women and 4 men

Then

4 x 3	7 x 6 x 5 x 4 = 6 x 35= 210
2 x 1	4 x 3 x 2 x 1

Assume 3 women and 3 men

Then

4 x 3 x 2	7 x 6 x 5 = 4 x 35 = 140
3 x 2 x 1	3 x 2 x 1

Assume 4 women and 2 men

Then

4 x 3 x 2 x 1	7 x 6 = 1 x 21 =21
4 x 3 x 2 x 1	2 x 1

371

66.

7	3	1	2	9	4	5	8	6
6	9	5	3	1	8	4	7	2
4	8	2	5	6	7	9	3	1
3	4	6	8	2	9	1	5	7
5	7	9	1	4	6	3	2	8
2	1	8	7	5	3	6	4	9
9	6	7	4	8	5	2	1	3
8	2	4	6	3	1	7	9	5
1	5	3	9	7	2	8	6	4

68. Met, Amaze, Chamber, and Team.

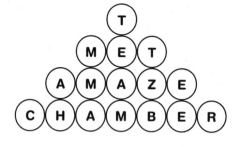

69. B. First letter contains two straight lines, second letter contains three straight lines, and third letter contains four straight lines.

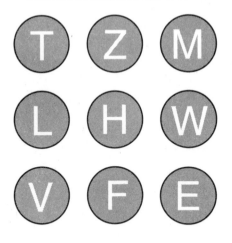

71. C.

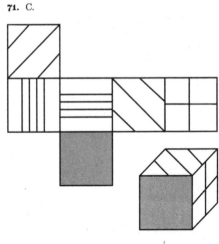

70. D. Different symbols in adjoining circles on the same row are carried into the circle between them in the row above. Similar symbols in the same place are dropped.

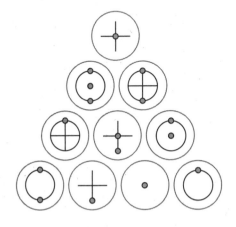

72. E.

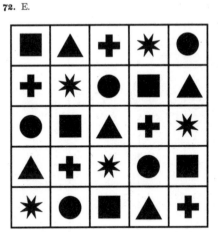

73. 'Die, my dear doctor, that's the last thing I shall do.' Lord Palmerston.

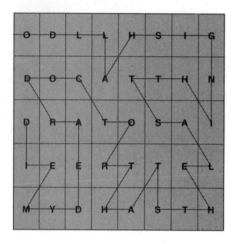

74. A.

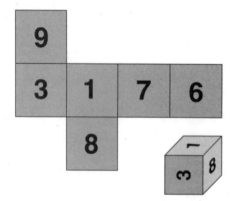

75. B. Start in the top circle. The series of arrows zigzags across in a downward direction with the arrows pointing as follows: right, left, up, up, down, left. This repeats.

76. ACT. All other three-letter words are spelled out by alternate letters of the six-letter words:

ODE	POODLE
ICE	CIRCLE
OAR	MOHAIR
USE	PURSUE
AIL	RADIAL
OLD	TOILED
ERR	NEARER
RAN	ORDAIN

77.

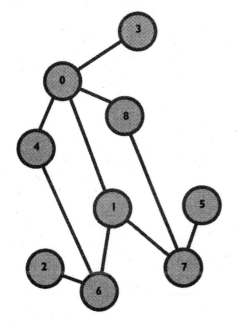

79. Crated and Carted

THE VALUABLE SCIENTIFIC

EQUIPMENT WAS

CAREFULLY CRATED AND

CHECKED BEFORE BEING

CARTED TO THE OTHER

SIDE OF THE BUILDING.

78. GONE WITH THE WIND – MARGARET MITCHELL

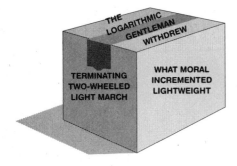

80. B (regurgitate, to vomit). The others are to restore or revive

81.

6	7	8	5	2	1	3	9	4
3	5	4	6	7	9	8	1	2
2	1	9	4	8	3	5	7	6
1	4	3	7	6	5	2	8	9
8	6	2	1	9	4	7	5	3
7	9	5	2	3	8	6	4	1
9	8	7	3	4	2	1	6	5
4	3	1	8	5	6	9	2	7
5	2	6	9	1	7	4	3	8

83. 50. The alphabetical values of the letters are added together.

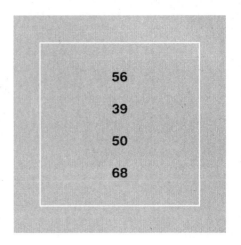

56

39

50

68

82. B.

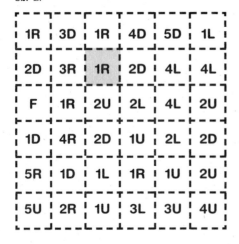

1R	3D	1R	4D	5D	1L
2D	3R	1R	2D	4L	4L
F	1R	2U	2L	4L	2U
1D	4R	2D	1U	2L	2D
5R	1D	1L	1R	1U	2U
5U	2R	1U	3L	3U	4U

84. Otter. A holt is an otter's home as a drey is a squirrel's home.

85. Top: Add the two digits of each number together to give the number of places the numbers move round.

Bottom: Add one to each number to give the amount of places each number moves around.

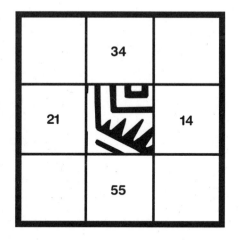

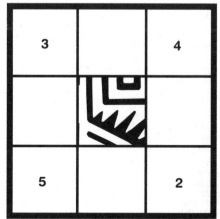

86.

87. 11.

5	6	3	9	8	2	1	4	7
7	1	4	5	3	6	8	9	2
9	2	8	1	4	7	3	5	6
3	9	2	6	7	8	4	1	5
4	8	7	2	1	5	6	3	9
6	5	1	3	9	4	7	2	8
8	3	9	7	2	1	5	6	4
1	7	6	4	5	9	2	8	3
2	4	5	8	6	3	9	7	1